Just Give Me a *Soft* Place to Land

a novel

JUDY CONDON

Book formatting by FormattedBooks.com

ISBN: 978-1-7349448-1-5 (paperback)
ISBN: 978-1-7349448-0-8 (eBook)

Prologue

They numbered only three when they gathered that first Wednesday night in the loft of Caroline's home in 1983. Three women, Beth, Sarah and Caroline, barely acquainted from varied backgrounds, met initially to simply enjoy a women's night out, a desire to share their passion for knitting and regale in the community of women.

Over the next thirty years their group would grow to seven in number. They would continue to gather each Wednesday evening but eventually, decades later, the group would move to a room on the first floor; some of the women, then in their seventies, no longer able to climb the stairs to the loft. They would continue to knit together and, over the course of decades, rejoice collectively as one in the group joyfully announced a family milestone. Conversely, they would provide compassion and solace when another sadly spoke of a loss.

As a sense of trust would develop within the group, so would a deep-seated bond among the women. From the first, the women would continue to feel safe enough to share, would speak of their past and their journeys; no two alike, but each journey embraced by others as though it were their own.

Beth

1983

At age forty, Beth had been married for eighteen years to her husband Ed. They lived in a spacious colonial home in a lovely neighborhood; their four children bright and well-behaved. She and Ed enjoyed a wealth of friends and, on the surface, appeared to the world to be a happily married couple. One might ask then, why had Beth been in therapy for over three years trying to peel away layers of sadness, rejection, shame, guilt and abandonment issues stemming from a single night twenty-four years earlier. She was hopeful that the therapy would help her overcome and put to rest all the demons she had carried since 1959. To those around her, her life appeared to be no different than other women she knew- rewarding and wonderful. It wasn't. She was desperate to fix it but didn't know how; how to make her life anything other than what it was…a disaster.

Beth's life was about to change dramatically. As Beth pushed her shopping cart in the grocery store one Saturday afternoon, a woman approached her from the opposite direction. The woman moved her cart beside Beth's, indicating she wanted to speak with her.

The woman introduced herself as Caroline and asked, "Excuse me. Do you mind telling me where you get your hair cut?"

Beth smiled, thanked her for the compliment, explaining, "Hi Caroline. My name is Beth. I've always cut my own hair." Caroline laughed and continued, obviously interested in prolonging their meeting. "Are you a hairdresser?"

"No, I'm in education," Beth responded. "I cut my own hair in part because I'm too busy to spend time at the hairdresser."

Caroline quickly offered, "I teach too. What grade do you teach?"

Beth responded, "I teach second grade over in Dayton but I've taught first grade and kindergarten too."

"What keeps you so busy outside of school?" Caroline asked.

"With a family and teaching, I find I don't have much time to do the things I like to do like read and knit."

Caroline quickly offered, "I've been a special education teacher for almost fourteen years. I love my job but it's very stressful. I love to read too but find knitting helps. Sometimes I just enjoy the comfort of the yarn in my hands. I find it helps relieve my stress. I've been thinking of starting a knitting group. Would you be interested?"

Beth immediately accepted the invitation. Caroline added, "I have a friend named Sarah who also loves to knit. I know she would be interested in joining us."

Caroline suggested they could meet at her house as she had a spacious finished loft area above an addition. After confirming that Wednesday night was an agreeable night, they exchanged addresses and phone numbers. Beth was thrilled at the prospect of meeting new women and assured Caroline she would enjoy meeting Sarah. Little did she know at that time that their group of three would eventually grow to seven over the years and would offer each of the women so much more than the exchange of knitting patterns and a lady's night out. As Caroline walked away, Beth chuckled to herself how a chance meeting in the grocery store, of all places, had resulted in the prospect of a knitting group and an opportunity to meet other women who shared her passion.

On that first Wednesday, each of the three women accomplished little knitting as they shared a bit about themselves. Sarah was the type of woman you felt you had known for years even though you had just met her.

"I've been married for twenty years and have two children. My husband, Rick, owns his own business. I'm embarrassed to admit, that I've never worked outside the home."

"Well, we won't hold that against you!" joked Beth.

Sarah laughed and added, "I love to decorate and collect 19thC antiques. Every weekend I go to flea markets and tag sales. Can't get enough of them! Rick never wanted me to work and said from the beginning, he would provide everything I needed and he's lived up to his word. I'm the oldest of three children and grew up in a small rural town where I met my husband. We got married before I was twenty."

"I think we have some things in common, Sarah. I grew up in a quiet little town too. My first husband, Bill, grew up in the same town and we married young, as well," Caroline offered.

"How many years have you been married, Caroline?" Beth asked.

"Bill and I were married twenty-three years but divorced when we became empty-nesters. I've been married to my second husband, Steve, for four years. I can relate to one or two of the rural 'small town' memories you spoke of, Sarah. I was in shock when I finished my teaching degree and was offered a job teaching in a larger inner-city school system. It was a real eye-opener.

"When I was hired, I had just graduated and was thankful to have been offered a job. I taught the classroom for emotionally disturbed children with nine boys aged seven to twelve. The school system was so large these children had been taken out of the classrooms as they were unmanageable. It was unbelievable! I was locked in a portable trailer with these kids as everyone had determined these children not only could not function in a regular classroom, they were a danger to their peers. It wasn't easy! They were tough kids and, by the end of the first day, I went home pretty beaten up. I had a bump on my forehead from being pushed into a column, a bruise on my right hip and a cut on my left shin where I was kicked!

"When my husband Bill got home from work and saw me, with wide-eyes he said, 'I think we should consider additional health insurance.'"

Both Sarah and Beth were visibly curious. "Caroline, you can't leave us hanging! What happened in that classroom?"

"Oh, it was a struggle and it took me some time to figure it all out, but by Christmas I had it all under control. Within the first few weeks, I caught one or two of the kids scraping the inside of the waste basket in the mornings, obviously hungry, so I brought in bowls and cereal. Sitting around the reading table having breakfast started the day and set the tone. It made all the difference in the world."

"How long have you taught special education?" Sarah asked.

"I've taught for almost fourteen years. I was offered a regular education position about five years ago in another town but turned it down because I felt I would be abandoning those children who so needed a caring adult figure in their lives. It's ironic that we're talking about this tonight because just last week I was approached by an educational publishing company and was offered a position with them as a sales representative. It is a huge decision and I've not yet sorted it all out."

"That's an exciting career path change," Beth commented enthusiastically. "What's your hesitancy if you don't mind me asking?"

"It's just a lot to consider. Giving up my tenure for one thing. Perhaps not being able to return to teaching if I found the sales position isn't something I want after all."

Beth remained quiet throughout most of the evening, seemingly more intent on listening rather than speaking, but did offer, "My husband Ed and I have four children. I've been teaching just a few years but hope someday to become an elementary principal."

The evening passed much too quickly and when Sarah suggested, "Want to meet the same time, same place next week?" There was instant agreement.

Weeks passed with the women sharing stories about their children, the latest book each had read and introducing their husband to the group through little warm, humorous stories.

Beth had not been anxious to share that first night, but after months was beginning to sense she needed support. She had been self-absorbed for weeks in her physical and emotional state. For some unexplained reason, she was being plagued by recurring dreams and unable to get back to sleep. She would awaken from a deep sleep feeling as though she was having a panic attack without any explanation as to why. It never occurred to her that the dreams and attacks might be caused by a change in hormones. Instead, Beth assumed it had more to do with the fact that she was suddenly being haunted by an event she thought she had left in her past long ago.

After six weeks of nearly sleepless nights, Beth began to show signs of sleep deprivation.

"Beth, do you feel alright?" Sarah asked. "You look a little peckish" - a word Sarah loved to use. Beth suddenly burst into tears, much to the surprise of Caroline and Sarah. They immediately hugged her with no questions being asked. Beth so needed their comfort and compassion – just a soft place to land.

Through her tears, Beth did her best to explain. "I know it seems that I have it all together, but that's not true. I have been in therapy for three years because of something that happened over twenty years ago… and I can't let it go. For the past few months, I've been having terrible nightmares almost every night and I'm so tired… emotionally exhausted."

Sarah asked, "Do you want to talk about it, Beth? You know we're both good listeners and it won't leave this room."

"His name is Jack", Beth offered. She could tell from the expression on their faces they had no idea what she was about to reveal but they were there to hear her. Once she started, she couldn't stop.

"Jack was my first boyfriend and my first love. I was only sixteen at the time. Almost every night, I have this same dream where I'm standing in a room with Jack and my husband Ed. In the dream, my husband is about to leave the room. With his hand on the door knob, he turns to me and asks, 'Beth, are you coming or are you staying?' I look longingly at Jack and answer Ed with the most resigned and forlorn voice, 'No I'm coming.' I leave the room with Ed then I awaken and am crying hysterically.

"Ed knows I'm awake but I can't tell him my dream. I can't admit that I've simply been emotionally unavailable to him during a large part of my marriage. I feel as though my dreams are sending me a message. How can I repeatedly want to stay with Jack rather than leave with Ed? The fact that in my dream I feel so much grief leaving with my husband, rather than staying with Jack, is haunting me."

Caroline and Sarah listened, absorbing what Beth had said, before Caroline gently asked,

"Do you know why Jack is so important to you after all this time?"

Beth looked up and through tears sobbed, "Because I was pregnant with his child when I was sixteen." No one spoke. Beth continued, "Pictures are beginning to appear in my mind of the baby I gave away. In my dreams, there is a baby with its arms outstretched to me to come get it; to come pick it up, to hold it. I am so troubled I have begun to experience severe anxiety attacks in the middle of the night. I wake up and pace around the living room or take cold showers at three in the morning hoping to stop the heat I feel rushing inside me. It starts at the base of my spine and travels upward through my chest until I think I'm going to have a heart attack. Sometimes it is so frightening, I feel as though I'm having a nervous breakdown and will have to be put into an institution."

"Oh Beth, my heart goes out to you," said Caroline. I can't imagine what you're going through, but I can see how painful it is for you. I'm glad you felt safe enough to share it. Is there anything we can do to help you other than always be here to listen?"

Caught up in the emotional revelation of the moment, Caroline added, "I know you both realize my husband Steve isn't my first husband. I managed to not get pregnant when I was a teenager, but I've kept secrets for lots of years too, from even my own children about my marriage to Steve.

"Steve was diagnosed with alcoholism, but I think suffers from severe psychological problems. I am never sure what is going to happen day to day. He does strange things if I'm late getting home from work. Sometimes he drinks too much but most times he doesn't. I just never know what I'll find when I come home from being anywhere. A few weeks ago, I was so scared he would hurt me, I had to run out of the house in the middle of the night."

"What?" Beth asked incredulously. "I know you'll tell us when you're ready to. I can't imagine how terrified you must have been! Listen to us! Are you safe?"

"Yes. I feel safe," replied Caroline. I'll tell you about it but right now it's still too hard to talk about it. Give me some time."

"It sounds to me as though we each have a journey to share ", added Sarah. "Maybe we can use our knitting time to help one another since we all feel safe here. I think it helps to talk, don't you? Maybe we can think of Caroline's loft as our safe haven since it seems we could all use a soft place to land."

At the end of the night, they hugged each other.

"Beth, if you awaken again from nightmares or attacks before the next meeting, please feel you can call me if you need to… even if it was in the middle of the night. We're here for you." Caroline assured her.

When Beth opened her heart, she opened the door to the others to use the knitting group as a platform for sharing.

On the following Wednesday night, the three had hardly sat down and pulled out their yarn, when Sarah turned to Beth and asked, "Was this week any better for you, Beth, with your nightmares?"

"Yes, it was, I think. It wasn't as frightening knowing I had you both to lean on if I needed to. It made a difference. Thanks for your support last week and for listening."

After sharing the latest pattern for a cable knit sweater she was knitting, Beth started to share her past.

"I got thinking afterward, I probably shocked you last week when I told you I had been pregnant as a teenager. I trust you both though and as hard as it's going to be to talk about it, I know it will help. You can probably give me a different perspective on how to deal with it all. I need to go all the way back to my parents, who weren't demonstrative individuals. My siblings and I knew we were loved, but hugs and kisses were not part of my parents' emotional makeup. There were perfunctory kisses goodnight or goodbye but seldom, if ever, a smile and show of joy at anything we shared at the dinner table or talked about during a car ride.

At dinner, we were expected to sit at the table while my father related the events of his day. Sitting and listening to tale after tale of his daily accomplishments gave me time to daydream about what was happening in my world, interrupted only if my father raised his voice to tell my brother, seated at his left, to 'Sit up straight and bring your food to your mouth.' As soon as dinner was over, I couldn't wait to escape to the safety of my bedroom."

"If your parents were like mine, we weren't allowed to leave the table unless our plate was clean, no matter what we had been served. My mother was a good cook, but she cooked to please my father and he loved liver and bacon! I can gag even now just thinking about having to swallow that before I could be excused," Caroline added. Beth and Sarah nodded in agreement.

Beth continued. "I was sixteen and a sophomore in high school. I remember that everything began on April 4th during our high school math class. Can you believe it? Twenty-five years later I can still remember the date. What does that tell you? Mr. D was blabbing on about a+ something and b equaling something else and no one was paying any attention. I was concentrating on the closeness of Jack sitting to my right and trying to control what I was feeling inside, completely ignoring the math lesson. Jack was good at everything. He was captain of the football team, President of the Student Council, president of our class. He was muscular, over 6' tall with broad shoulders. His blue eyes sometimes looked as though he was very serious, almost scowling, deep in thought. Jack had short dark blond hair which he wore in a popular style back then called a flat top. He had a great smile. He walked with confidence, but was subdued. Jack never deliberately drew attention to himself as he didn't have to. He was a hero among his peers."

"He sounds terrific, Beth! Tell us more!" urged Sarah enthusiastically.

"Oh, believe me. He was! Jack leaned over and placed a note on my desk. It was a scribbled message asking me if I wanted to go to a movie on Saturday night – a date. A date with the captain of the football team, the president of the Student Council, the tallest and best- looking guy in the entire school as far as I was concerned…. and most of the other girls in our class would agree."

"I could hardly wait until Saturday. I spent half the afternoon getting ready for my big date. My heart was pounding. I couldn't decide whether to wear the gray flannel skirt with the moss green sweater or the black skirt and white blouse. My hair was turned in rollers for the better part of the two hours before he was picking me up. I purposely sat down at the piano when I heard his car in the driveway. I wanted to have him hear me playing when he rang the doorbell, hoping I could impress him with my talent. I introduced him to my parents then quickly hurried him out the door. We drove to the movie theater in his mother's pale blue Ford sedan, talking the entire way about classmates, our teachers and of course football.

"We dated all summer sometimes attending parties, going to drive-in movies or just gathering with friends at the beach. We both had summer jobs during the day but spent every available evening together. His parent's home was small with a little cabin in the shade of the backyard where Jack had moved during the heat of the summer. There were nights when, after a party, we would stop by his 'place' and enjoy the privacy of just spending time with each other. We were basically inseparable. In early August,

I turned sixteen and my parents rented the local country club and hired a live band for my sweet sixteenth party."

"Wow, lucky you, Beth. A sweet sixteen party with a band. My parents didn't do anything special on my sixteenth except have a family picnic," Caroline recalled.

"Yeah it was nice. I had a new dress and felt pretty. Jack and I danced together for most of the night. It felt a little strange to be the center of attention as the 'birthday girl', but glad to be noticed as 'Jack's girl'. At the close of the party, Jack pulled me aside and handed me a lovely gift-wrapped box. I opened it slowly and gasped when I found an opal ring with two tiny diamonds on either side. It was gorgeous. I hugged him and thanked him profusely, hoping that the ring signified a serious commitment on his part."

"What did your parents say when you showed them the ring Jack gave you?" asked Caroline.

"I don't think they thought anything about it. At least I have no recollection that it created any type of reaction. But now that you mention it, maybe Jack's gift played into a decision they made and told me a few weeks later," Beth replied.

"Later that month, my parents sat me down and informed me they intended to send me to a small local private school for my junior and senior high school years. They explained they felt I could get a more exceptional education than I would get at our public high school.

"Clearly the decision was made and I had little to say about it. I was devastated and resentful, immediately recognizing it as a means, on their part, to separate me from my friends. Maybe it was to separate me from Jack as well, but I had no say in the matter. I left the room and went to the piano where I sat stunned, soulfully playing, 'When You Walk Through a Storm'. My enthusiasm to return to school was gone. I made up my mind they might be able to send me to another school, but they could not separate me from my friends. I was going to keep seeing my friends and go to the high school activities even if I wasn't able to attend the high school during the day for classes."

"Why didn't you speak up and say something?" wondered Caroline.

"You don't understand yet about my father. Just wait. My father was not someone you spoke up to. You'll see.

"The private school was an all-girls school housed in an old inner- city mansion; the classes were held in what would have been originally a sitting room or large bedroom on the second floor. We had to wear a uniform: a plaid pleated skirt, white cotton blouse, knee socks and saddle shoes. In less than a month, I had gone from being a member in a class of hundreds to a class of nine. I knew, before the end of the first week, I didn't belong there. I wasn't like any of those girls. I barely spoke to them and not once in a over several weeks could I find anything we had in common."

"What made the girls different?"

"Sarah, they were snobby. They were fake. Even their conversations sounded like they just wanted to make sure everyone knew their family was rich.

"Weekends were what I lived for. I remember the third Saturday in September. It started out as any other Saturday. Right after breakfast, as always, I was getting ready to go to the football game and watch Jack play. He was a star on the football team and I loved sitting in the stands watching him play. Everyone knew he was my boyfriend and it made me feel so good. I was so proud that Jack was my boyfriend. After the game, my friends and I always went to the local diner where we hung out, reliving the highlights of the game over burgers and fries. Then, we would go home and get ready for our dates that night.

"Jack picked me up around seven that night and we ended up driving down to the shore where we sat by the beach talking about the game. Jack often talked with me about his dreams and how his path was going to take him after college to the Air Force Academy in Colorado where he would earn his pilot's license and fly for a major airline. Listening to him, you would think it was a sure thing; and maybe it was at that point, at least in his mind, since there was nowhere Jack didn't excel whether it was in academics or sports. He had the respect of the school faculty, as well as his classmates. And…I was his girl! Even after five months, I couldn't believe that he loved me. For the first time, I felt emotional connection. It felt so good to be loved. His warmth and affection convinced me I was lovable. It was all new to me. I had never felt anyone connect to me emotionally as Jack did. He was my soulmate and, in my young foolish way of looking at things, knew my heart belonged to him. He was my first love and the first male who had demonstrated any feelings of love for me. I was ecstatic!"

"There's nothing that compares to that first love is there?" Sarah commented.

"No. I don't know if it was our age, how good it felt to feel loved or just teenage hormones, but even though we were physically attracted to each other, we hadn't done anything but kiss. We sat for a while that night at the beach when Jack leaned over and suggested, 'Let's drive to the other side of town. There's a full moon and it's going to be beautiful on top of the hill.' We reached a quiet spot, got out of the car and were able to see a path which we took to walk to a clearing on the hillside. Jack was right. The view of the full moon was spectacular, and the hill overlooked the city below which was filled with thousands of white lights."

"I think I know what you're going to say," Sarah said.

"Jack guided me to a spot on the ground where we could watch the moon. We sat down and, as I turned to say something, he took me in his arms. He pressed into me; his arms were strong and totally wrapped me in his hug. He kissed me passionately using his tongue. I had never been kissed like this before. The only time I had ever been kissed was when I was thirteen and went to a dance with a boy, I didn't care for at all. After he brought me home, we were standing in the driveway and he kissed me on the lips. Nothing like what Jack was doing!"

"I think we always remember our first kiss," Caroline commented.

"I kissed Jack back and felt things happening in my body that I had never felt before! I began to feel a tingling. I tried to catch my breath but he didn't stop. His hands moved up and down my back before reaching under my shirt and unhooking my bra. He gently laid me down and lay beside me where I felt his hardness pressing into my hip. I still didn't know what was going to happen, but I liked what I was feeling. With the moonlight, I could see his face and he was smiling. His eyes were looking into mine. Without looking away, he unbuttoned my blouse and when he touched me, I started to breath heavier as the tingling sensation intensified."

"I'm starting to get a little excited, Beth!" laughed Sarah.

"I didn't know how long I could wait. I wanted more. I wanted it all. I was panting. He took my hand and put a condom in it and I had no idea what I was supposed to do with it. He guided my hand and helped me place it over him. As he moved on top of me, I was so ready to open myself to him. I wanted to have inside me without any thought as to what repercussions there might be. He paused, looked at me and asked, 'Are you sure?' I could barely answer. 'Yes' I nodded. 'I want to. I love you and want to be close. I want you to know how much I love you.'"

"He entered me slowly at first. I felt a sharp pain and let out a small gasp, but he was gentle. He knew that this was my first time, and although I physically wanted more, I could tell he didn't want to hurt me. He smiled at me as he entered me entirely and started to move faster until I felt an end to the tingling and he moaned."

Caroline and Sarah had stopped knitting, caught up in Beth's story and anxious to hear more. While Beth went to refill her coffee cup, Caroline shared, with a chuckle, her first sexual encounter.

"I confess my first experience was nothing in comparison. I even questioned what the big deal with sex was all about!"

Sarah nodded in agreement and went on to confess, "Mine was about the same as what you described, Caroline. It wasn't until years later I learned what an orgasm was all about!"

They laughed. Beth sat down and picked up where she had ended.

"A month later, I realized that my period was late. I figured it was because of the stress of the new school. I didn't pay much attention, but just in case, I began to take hot baths thinking that would start my period. It didn't help. I started to feel panicky, but waited two weeks before saying anything. Jack and I had been invited to our friend Jane's house on the last Saturday night in November and were sitting on the couch in her living room after everyone had left. I sat beside him and told him that I had missed my period, but wasn't worried because I couldn't possibly be pregnant since we had used a condom. He looked puzzled but didn't seem overly concerned. I thought nothing of his reaction at the time."

"Did it help to tell him, Beth? Did you feel better that he knew?" asked Sarah.

"What was his reaction?" added Caroline.

Beth hesitated before answering and then replied, "I remember thinking he seemed pretty calm when I told him, although I also remember he had a puzzling expression like he was trying to understand what I was saying and figure out how my period being late had anything to do with that night. At least, that's how I interpreted his expression. I felt better once I had told him since I now had someone who shared my concern."

Beth began to sob uncontrollably.

Caroline and Sarah each jumped up to hand Beth a tissue and shot each other a glance. They waited in silence, caught up in Beth's revelation and the pain she continued to experience. After bringing Beth a glass of water, Caroline did her best to move the conversation into something lighter to soften the mood and give Beth a chance to catch her breath.

"Ah, I have some good news to share. My oldest daughter just got accepted at the college that was her first choice. She worked hard to get there and we're really proud of her and excited."

"Tell her congratulations, Caroline. That's great," Sarah said.

Beth took a deep breath and said, "The next morning I had just gotten home from church when the phone rang. It was Jack's mother. She said, 'I just found a note on Jack's bed. He said you might be pregnant. He ran away last night. Can you come over?'"

"So, I went and I'll tell you next week the rest but, I think I've monopolized the conversation enough tonight, girls. I'm exhausted. Yeah Caroline, tell her congratulations from me too."

The ladies decided to call it a night and hugged each other as they descended the stairs, offering Beth a special squeeze.

The next week, when the ladies gathered, Caroline appeared anxious and within minutes of all sitting down, she opened the conversation.

"Just hearing you talk about getting a call from Jack's mother and her telling you he had run away that night, brings back terrible memories for me about what my husband did one night to me", Caroline sighed. "I'm embarrassed, and a little ashamed to tell you what he did because sometimes I question what part I played in what happened. I'm struggling to convince myself that I didn't cause it and I couldn't cure it."

Beth and Sarah continued to knit, hoping their activity would allow Caroline the time to gather her thoughts and courage to continue.

Caroline took a deep breath, "The night I'm talking about happened about six weeks ago not long before I met you both, but I didn't feel comfortable telling you about it then because I was embarrassed. After hearing about what Beth has gone through, I know I can trust you both."

"It was four o'clock in the morning. I was sitting in a rocking chair in the corner of the room off the kitchen. The police were just leaving. As the officers passed by me, one officer turned toward me and said, 'You need to take your dog and find somewhere else to stay tonight. We opened the windows in the basement but the smell is strong. It's not healthy for you to stay here.'"

"I nodded acknowledging that I had heard, but, even then, couldn't imagine finding somewhere to go. Maybe if I had had you both then it would have been different, but I had no one - not friends or family. No one had any idea what my situation is like with Steve. I've kept my life hidden from everyone, always smiling in public, but behind my smile I carry a lot of pain."

"Why were the police in your kitchen at four o'clock in the morning, Caroline?" Sarah wanted to know.

"Steve did something terrible and I had to leave the house in the middle of night. I have managed to keep my problems hidden from even my grown children who live nearby. Even though horrible things had happened in the past six hours, I didn't want to leave my home because that was where I felt safer than anywhere else. I sat in the chair staring into space, shivering, but not because it was February and the basement windows were open. I remember my dog was huddled at my feet and looked scared. I reached down and petted his head trying to assure him that we were safe and we didn't have to be scared anymore but I wasn't convincing myself. I was in shock, shaking and terrified of what was going to happen. When I was finally alone, I started to cry."

"Caroline, what happened? Wasn't there someone you could call to come stay with you?" Beth asked.

"No. I am telling you…no one knew what I was living with. There was one woman, Ann, who had known Steve for years, long before I had, and she had become someone I knew I could trust. So even though it was 3:00 o'clock in the morning, I called her and she got to my house just as the ambulance was leaving the driveway taking Steve to the hospital. It had started to snow which was accumulating quickly on the frozen ground. Ann stayed with me for an hour but was unable to stay longer as she had scheduled a business flight that morning.

"I told Ann what had happened and she quickly tried to assure me that everything was going to be alright, 'Steve is in good hands,' she said. 'There's no need to rush to him. The hospital is the best place for him right now. The nurses will give him something to calm him down and if he was drunk, he'll sober up.'

"As she hugged me, she said, 'Please do what the police say. Go to a friend's house or motel. I understand why you want to stay in your house, but it's not safe. At least if you're going to stay, make sure you open the bedroom window and get some fresh air in that room. Steve was always willing to have a good time and we both know he occasionally drinks too much, but I think this is a single incident and something that won't ever happen again.'"

"I said, 'I really want to believe what you're saying, Ann. Maybe you're right. Maybe I should stay away and stop enabling him by rushing to the hospital. Maybe I can send him a message that his behavior has been unacceptable.'"

"Ann apologized, 'I feel terrible that I have to leave you alone like this, but I'll call you later in the day.'"

"As Ann turned to leave, she urged me strongly, 'Let him sit there, Caroline. You need to start taking care of yourself.'"

"As Ann left, I began to pace around the room trying to burn off a mass of built- up emotional energy. I was torn. It wasn't that I was afraid to be alone, but I was afraid of the future. The unknown was terrifying, especially with no one I could turn to."

"What did he do, Caroline?" Sarah asked. "Is he sick?"

"He isn't sick like how you may be thinking. But I think he does have some problems and that night, he got scared and called the police when I wasn't there." Caroline explained.

"Is he alright now? I wished you had known us then, Caroline. You could have called either of us and we would have been there for you," Sarah said. Beth nodded in agreement.

"He's home from the hospital and doing alright."

"Well, that's good news. What did you end up doing? Did you listen to your friend Ann and stay home?" Beth asked.

"I was still in my pajamas under my coat and didn't know what I should do. I didn't know if I should get dressed, get in my car while it was still dark out and drive to the hospital to 'rescue' my husband or wait until the snow stopped and it was light out. I was the wife who always tried to be strong and make everything 'all better', but that night I didn't know what to do. Nothing like this had ever happened to me. Part of me thought I should be by my husband's side as any good wife would be, but then part of me was scared and it turned to anger. I wanted to leave him there and pretend nothing had happened. Why should I rush to go to him after what he did to me? I tried to justify my action by asking myself what any 'good wife' would do in the same situation but then I decided not just any 'good wife' had lived through what I had.

As Caroline reached for a tissue, Sarah handed her a cup of tea. She and Beth remained silent, as clearly there was more to the story. Caroline took a deep breath and continued.

"Ann left and I was alone with my dog. I didn't know what I wanted to do first. Part of me wanted to clean up the mess in the kitchen, make the room look neat and clean again as it had twenty-four hours ago. Maybe then I could pretend the last six hours had been just a bad dream. It was five o'clock and I knew there was no way I was going to be able to go to sleep. I was cold and thought a cup of tea sounded good. I turned the teapot on and thought to myself a cup of tea is going to make me feel better. Then I'll start to clean up the kitchen. Before the water boiled, my telephone rang."

"My gosh, who could possibly call you at that hour? I hope it was good news," said Sarah, anxious and nervous about Caroline's answer.

"That was my immediate reaction, too. I couldn't imagine who could possibly be calling me at five in the morning. I hesitated to answer but thought the not knowing would be worse. I answered and after confirming my identity, the woman on the other end of the line wasted no time attacking me verbally. With her sense of frustration clearly emanating over the phone lines, she told me in no uncertain terms, 'This is the hospital. If you don't get here in the next hour, we are admitting your husband to the psychiatric ward.' I could clearly hear Steve in the background shouting nearly incoherent obscenities. Before I could respond, the line went dead."

"Caroline, what was wrong with him? From what you're describing it sounds like he's a madman. Had he been drinking or doing drugs?" Beth asked.

"I didn't know what had happened. It took me a while to reconstruct in my mind what triggered the behavior that night. I began to put together other events and realized there was a pattern. I could see the pattern but I didn't know how to fix it. Part of me wanted to race to the hospital and part of me, the angry and frightened part, never wanted to see him again. My fear had turned to anger. In hindsight, I think the best thing I should have done was to have left Steve where he was and let them admit him to the psychiatric ward. But I was the 'solutions' wife, always looking for a way to overcome a problem and my need to 'fix' things took over."

"Did you go?" both women asked simultaneously.

"For the first time since nine o'clock the night before, I got out of my pajamas and got dressed. I left the dog, grabbed my boots and gloves, and shuffled carefully down the snow-covered driveway to my car still parked at the curb where I had left it in the early hours of the morning."

"Why was your car parked in the street, Caroline, from the night before?" Beth asked.

"I'm getting to that part. I had to leave the house the night before because Steve was out of control and I was scared. I left it in the street," Caroline explained.

"I was less afraid of driving to the hospital in the snowstorm than I was of what was going to happen when I got there. There was no one I could tell. I felt I had to conceal my problems from everyone or risk admitting to the world I had made a terrible costly mistake. I was embarrassed and even ashamed. I had tried to give everyone the impression that I had married a wonderful, loving man, who adored me and we were going to live happily ever after. I didn't know how to fix my life even though I thought of myself as a 'fixer'. The worst part was that I couldn't turn to anyone for help or a shoulder."

By the time Caroline finished talking she was sobbing and looking to Beth and Caroline for a hug and comfort. Without yet knowing the complete story of that night, they surmised it was as she had described. She had simply left the house because Steve had been out of control and she was scared. Beth and Sarah moved to sit on either side of her as she bowed her head and sobbed. Neither asked Caroline for the specifics as they hoped that Caroline would continue another time when she felt comfortable. Once assured that Caroline was alright, the three women squeezed each other's hand and, with a last embrace, Beth and Caroline thanked Sarah for sharing, recognizing how painful it was to do so.

"Is he alright now, Caroline?" Sarah asked.

"Yes. He's getting some help."

"That story took a lot of courage to share, Caroline," said Sarah.

Relieved to hear from Caroline that her husband was alright, Beth reassured Caroline, "We'll be here for you if you ever want to talk about that night again. Maybe sharing can help. I know it made a difference to talk about my nightmares with you both," added Beth.

As the women continued to meet faithfully each Wednesday, little by little their journeys began to gradually unfold. Interspersed with serious discussions and painful admissions, there were moments of laughter as the women exchanged humorous tales involving their children, suggested favorite novels, shared reactions to the latest funny sitcom they had watched or loving silly antidotes about a spouse.

One night, Caroline started the evening by sharing a hysterical event that had happened with her students that day!

"Remember last week I mentioned that I had asked the principal if I could take the students on a field trip to the airport? I thought the kids would enjoy seeing planes and even ride an escalator which would be a new experience. Well we went today! The kids were great! They all fit in my Volkswagen bus and they seemed in awe during the forty-five-minute ride. We got to the airport and I took them through the terminal, up the escalator to the large windows overlooking the tarmac. There was a large plane out on the tarmac and, as I looked out at the plane, unable to believe my eyes, there was Eric, one of my students, at the top of the portable stairs, at the entrance of the plane, waving to me!!! I almost died!! I ran down the stairs to the doorway, the other children following me, laughing loudly. I motioned for Eric to come over immediately. Proud of his accomplishment and not really wanting to fly to St. Louis, he sauntered over."

"What would you have done, Caroline, if he didn't come over? Oh my gosh, you must have been in shock!" Sarah said. "You must have been ready to ground Eric for life! Did you ever tell the principal?"

"Eric spent the next two days in 'time out', and when I told the principal, his eyes were as large as saucers! We both had a good laugh recognizing that no one was hurt and joked that neither one of us would have wanted to go to St. Louis to get him."

The levity of Caroline's experience endeared her further to Sarah, who was concerned about Beth and Caroline's well-being after hearing a portion of their stories, but she felt confident they would speak up if either needed to. Sarah would never have urged either woman to reveal more of their journey as it was a given fact that sharing was up to the individual. After months of listening to Caroline and Beth share, Sarah felt she was ready to open up about her past as the bond among the three women had continued to strengthen.

"Beth you've talked about the tremendous guilt you've felt and I need to say, I understand what you're saying because I have the same problem. I guess I should say I *had* the same problem. I was suffering from such guilt there were times I didn't think I could keep going. The pain was so severe", Sarah confessed. "I guess it doesn't matter what causes guilt because the sensation is the same, but I know what caused mine. Not once but twice, I did something that I so deeply regretted, but by the time I had a chance to change it, it was too late. The guilt I felt was suffocating.

"In the fall of 1961, I was a freshman at a two-year women's college located in a small village in Maine. My parents chose the school even though I would have preferred a college in a city where there might be more to do. I was overruled and they rationalized that their choice offered a greater selection of courses and was rated in the top three best junior women's colleges in the country. The campus was privately situated on a hill which served to offer panoramic views of the surrounding mountains, particularly in the fall when the foliage was at its peak.

"The dormitories and administrative buildings were built in a large circle surrounding a grassed area we called the 'quad'. The campus provided everything a student would need so there was seldom any reason to leave 'the hill', but often on Sunday mornings, some of us walked down the hill to the village for church or to enjoy a home-cooked breakfast at the country inn. I was raised in the Catholic faith where, whether or not to attend church on Sunday was never a consideration, I walked down the hill to the little stone church each Sunday. Although the service was not Catholic, I welcomed the sense of peace I felt with the final blessing in the service. I felt as though the service set the tone for a positive beginning of each new week.

"In November, I returned to college after a horrendous Thanksgiving weekend at home. I came back to campus feeling such pain that I tried everything I could, without relief, to stop feeling the way I did. I was anxious and my restlessness overpowered me. I was so desperate to put an end to my anxiety; I was unable to concentrate on anything else - almost catatonic."

"What happened to you over Thanksgiving, Sarah? Was it something with your parents? I remember how coming home from college and being under my parent's eye was a big adjustment."

"No, it wasn't my parents, Beth."

"After two weeks back at school, with no one else to turn to, one evening after dinner I telephoned the pastor at the stone church and asked if he had time to see me. I added I was at the college and would walk down to the village if he could see me right then. I was frantic for someone, anyone, to relieve me from my pain. I didn't know where to turn. Talking with friends hadn't helped. I recognized my parents were both physically and emotionally unavailable. I was at a college, essentially in the middle of the woods alone. I had not been at school long enough to make close friends, certainly no one I could trust to give me a shoulder or the comfort I needed. There was no one on the faculty I knew well enough to speak with, which left me with no one other than the pastor.

"I knocked on the rectory door which was opened immediately by a housekeeper who directed me into a small office at the end of the hallway. She motioned me to take a seat in the stuffed armchair to the left. I waited for a few moments, and stood when the pastor entered the room then sat down after he took the other seat. I introduced myself. The pastor turned to me and asked in a gentle soft voice, 'What can I do for you Sarah?' The flood gates opened and I poured out my heart, barely stopped long enough through my uncontrollable crying to catch my breath. I held nothing back, begging him to tell me how I could feel at peace."

"What had happened to you, Sarah? I'm worried," Caroline voiced her concern.

"I was in such pain because I was feeling guilty that I hadn't done something over Thanksgiving weekend that I thought I could and I wasn't ever going to have a chance to make it better. We talked for a long time, at least it seemed so to me. I ran out of words; how many different ways could I ask for peace? The pastor listened, interrupting me a few times, but usually just allowed me to speak and cry. I have no recollection of his exact words, just his soft tone of voice. I remember he tried to assure me that grief was a natural emotion. I knew that. He wanted me to believe that God had everything under control. I so wanted to believe that too but I couldn't bring myself to wholeheartedly accept that when I was in such pain. If God was there why was I in such distress? The pastor emphatically stressed that it was not our place to question or doubt His plan. My Catholic upbringing had taught me that, as well. The pastor's final words were that it was our duty to accept the direction of the higher power, as He knew all. I felt such extreme bitterness and anger listening. I wanted to scream in frustration. This wasn't what I wanted to hear. This wasn't making the pain go away. I felt no different than when I had walked in the door."

"At the end of an hour, I recognized that I was not going to find what I needed there. I suspect the pastor came to the same realization. I was exhausted, emotionally spent. I stood to leave. Nothing the pastor said reached me. None of his assurances about God knowing best offered me freedom from my grief and guilt. As I put my hand on the door knob of his office, he stood and asked in a soft voice, 'Have I helped you my child?' I turned, looked at him and answered, 'No. I'm sorry'. I walked out without looking back."

"What was his reaction, Sarah? Did he try to make you stay and talk more?" Caroline asked. "How sad that the pastor had no words of consolation where you really needed them."

"I know what you mean about feelings of guilt, Sarah", added Beth. "Nothing anyone can say helps the pain go away. I think letting go of the guilt comes from within and the only words that help are those that lead you to forgiving yourself."

Sarah nodded in agreement and said, "If it's okay, I want to keep going. There are more things from my childhood, after all this time, that I think had a tremendous effect on me.

"My memories of childhood were for the most part happy ones. I was one of four children so there was always activity in the house with family and our friends. My parents were very active socially and had a variety of groups of friends, bridge players to tennis players. As a result, my parent's weekends were filled with social activities. Rather than hire a babysitter, my siblings and I spent most weekends at our maternal grandparents.

"My mother was an only child which might explain why her parents welcomed the opportunity to have us spend weekends with them. We would be dropped off on Friday nights and joined by my parents on Sunday early afternoon where we would all play some type of family game while my grandmother prepared our traditional family Sunday dinner. I look back with fondness for those Sundays as they occurred in 'the old days' before malls were open on

Sundays, and Sundays were recognized as special family days. After a game of cards or perhaps Chinese checkers before dinner, my grandmother called us to their large dining room table where I was given the seat of honor to the right of my grandfather, who sat at the head. Dinner was always served early enough for us to enjoy our favorite Sunday night television show,' Lassie'."

Reminiscing a bit, Beth and Caroline agreed that 'Lassie' had been their favorite childhood show, as well, followed by a show called 'You Asked for It'. Sarah smiled briefly inwardly relieved that both women were listening and tuned into all that she was sharing.

"My grandmother was so special to me. She was probably the most loving adult in my childhood. She had so many talents and always made me a part of whatever she was doing, no matter if she was baking, sewing or weeding the garden. Her outfit was always the same. She was a tiny woman, not even five feet tall, and I never saw her dressed in anything else but a floral collared, short-sleeved rayon dress with buttons down the front. She was never without stockings nor her black laced shoes with thick, square inch high heels.

"We called her Grammy. She was an exceptional cook, always preparing everything she made from scratch. She was active in her church and through the church was often hired to bake pot pies which she prepared in a narrow galley-like pantry off the kitchen. The income from her pies helped supplement my grandfather's income from his gas station. I remember days where there were as many as two hundred pot- pies she had baked for a bride's wedding meal. Once baked and placed on large metal trays, the pies were temporarily stored on the enclosed side porch to cool, waiting for someone to pick them up."

"Wow, Sarah. I can picture her from your description. What talent!" Beth commented.

"I know I'm talking about my grandmother a lot but she was clearly the warmest adult in my life. In addition to the pot-pies, my grandmother made almost all the cakes for every wedding at her church. Each cake was flawlessly decorated and edged with frosting she had piped on the top rim and base of the cakes. On more than one occasion, I recall sneaking into my grandmother's pantry with my brother where we carefully opened one of the plastic containers of cake decorations she kept neatly stacked on the shelves. Our favorites were the small hard silver beads she placed in the centers of decorative drops of frosting. The beads were plentiful enough in the containers that any missing beads would not be noticed. The most delicate decorations though were the hard sugar- formed miniature purple and yellow pansies and pink roses which we, even at our young age, thought too beautiful to eat."

"I hope she shared some of her recipes," exclaimed Beth.

"I'm glad you asked because I have a metal box with all of her recipes, written in her hand which I would recognize anywhere. My mother was a great cook, too, so I think Grammy passed along her love of cooking. I, on the other hand, don't mind cooking, but I tend to just haphazardly throw ingredients in the pot!"

"Ah. A woman after my own heart!" laughed Caroline.

"When not in her kitchen, Grammy spent a lot of time in a small room upstairs that she used for sewing. It was a bright room; I think probably at one time a second story enclosed porch, as there were windows on three of the four walls. My grandmother's black Singer sewing machine stood in front of one window giving her ample light as she fed the fabric through the needle. The needle on the sewing machine was operated with the movement of a treadle that she rocked feverishly back and forth with her feet as she effortlessly created aprons in brightly colored fabrics which she sold at the annual church fair. If I was sitting with her, she often gave me scraps of fabric to play with to keep me out of trouble. I can still hear the sound of her machine and pedal."

"Where did your grandparents live, Sarah?"

"Caroline, they had the most beautiful place. Their house was on the shore of Long Island Sound in Connecticut. There was a spectacular view of the water from a large window in the living room, but we spent most summer days under the awning of the wraparound porch. As my grandfather rocked in the corner, keeping an eye on us as young children, and his black Spaniel, Bonnie, at his heel, my grandmother seemingly pulled out of the air endless treasures that kept us entertained for hours. A large collection of buttons kept us intrigued while we built houses with her hundreds of old German decorative playing cards."

"They must have loved to have you visit them every weekend," Beth said.

"Their lawn sprawled over one hundred yards long from the edge of the porch to the seawall below at ocean's edge. In addition to baking and sewing, my grandmother was an avid gardener and maintained numerous flowerbeds bordering each side of the yard- and not a weed to be found in any. In the center of the yard, two flowerbeds, filled solely with numerous varieties and colors of roses, were separated by a small shallow pool of water lilies. As I look back, it is beyond my imagination how my grandmother managed to accomplish all she did in the course of a day. I have to say it again - she was the sweetest grownup in my life. Never once do I remember her raising her voice or being impatient or angry with us."

"She sounds very sweet," Beth commented.

"She made it a point to include me. If she was baking, she came up with some way for me to help with the beating or if she was in the garden, she gave me little jobs so we were always together. I clearly had the sense that she liked spending time with me. I was given a job in her gardens and she made it sound as though her flowers were dependent on my job to survive! I was handed a soup can of kerosene and shown how I was to pick the Japanese beetles off the rose bush leaves and drop the beetles into the can. She emphasized the importance of my job, making me feel very special by pointing out to me the damaged pedals of the flowers which the beetles had eaten. Even today, I remember the lesson she gave me when I was probably seven or eight years old. She taught me the correct place to cut or prune the rose bushes by finding a cluster of five leaves and cutting the stem directly above it. I think of her every time I prune my rose bushes."

"I love roses," added Caroline, "especially yellow. They're my favorite."

"On one side of the yard, there was a storage shed where my grandfather kept his lawnmower and my grandmother's garden tools. It was a sizable shed, yet held few pieces of equipment, and therefore, easily emptied when I wanted to use the shed as my playhouse for my dolls. The outside had white painted shingles accented with dark green shutters on the windows. I have happy memories playing with my sisters and our dolls when we visited, as my grandparents gave us everything young children could ask for. Weekends became the high point of my childhood memories."

"I can see why! What kid wouldn't love that?" Beth nodded.

"My grandmother showed her love of us through her cooking and always made our favorite foods for each meal. There were always pancakes for breakfast that she cooked on the griddle on top of her oversized gas stove; meat and cheese sandwiches with whatever soup we wanted for lunch and often 'kid' food for supper like hot dogs or burgers. Everything my grandparents did let us know we were loved. Although we never doubted our parents love for us, neither our father nor mother were people who showed affection. My grandparents filled that void. I grew to look to my grandparents to compensate for what I needed as a child-especially from my grandmother."

"You are so lucky to have these wonderful memories of your grandparents, Sarah. My grandparents lived so far away, I saw them only at Christmas and a week or two in the summer," Caroline commented.

"I know. I was lucky, but I'm not sure I appreciated it until I was older. I was just a kid.

"Not only were my parents undemonstrative with affection, they exhibited little emotion between each other. When I was quite young, I remember seeing an occasional love tap on my mom's fanny by my dad and recall his calling her 'Muzzy' every once in a while, but those instances were few and a long time ago, though. By the time I was in high school, I began to sense that not only was there little warmth between them, my mother always seemed angry; reduced to emotional numbness, giving a minimal acknowledgement when my father spoke or recalled an event which had happened at work that day. He always ready to share an accomplishment, a humorous story or special event that took place during the day; she was often unable to share any."

"That's so sad, Sarah. Was it difficult for you to see this as a child?" Caroline wondered.

"I think my mother saw her role in keeping the house and being a mother. Looking back, I suspect the fact that my father wasn't an affectionate man saddened her greatly. I think she suffered from depression. It wasn't until I was an adult that I regretted I didn't do more to help her. My father was such a dominant figure in our family, my mother sadly lived in his shadow.

"Don't get me wrong. I wasn't aware of any fighting between my parents; they just seemed to exist together. I clearly remember one Sunday, though, at my grandparent's dinner table. Everyone at the table seemed to be happy and in a joyful mood. My sisters, brother and I thought it would be safe to join in on the fun and we started to tease my father and mimic him about his laughing with a lady after church in the parking lot when he walked her to her car. I'm sure it was innocent and his behavior meant nothing, but my mother suddenly threw down her napkin and ran up the stairs crying. We sat at the table stunned for a few minutes realizing that we had done something wrong, but too young to know what it was. My grandparents attempted to smooth over the incident laughing like it was all a joke, but looking back I recognize how uncomfortable they were. We were encouraged to finish our dinner while my father climbed the stairs to follow my mother. We proceeded to eat in silence with my grandparents until a short time later when my parents came back downstairs and told us to gather our things together. We were going home."

"Yikes, did you know what you had done?" Beth asked.

"No. It was so unusual that my father seemed in a good mood and was joking about something, we were just kids caught up in the moment and wanted to tease him and take part in the humor."

When Sarah finished talking about her visits to her grandparents on weekends, she had not shared what had caused her guilt, but Beth and Caroline appreciated that in good time, Sarah would when she was ready. The topic of grandparents triggered a memory for Caroline that she was anxious to share and lighten the mood.

"That reminds me of something that happened to me when I was about eighteen. It was one afternoon in the summer, my boyfriend and I decided to take our family's sailfish and put it on top of the car to go sailing off the coast of my grandparent's summer cottage. After sailing for a few hours, my grandparents invited us to join them on the porch for a drink. Neither my boyfriend nor I was accustomed to cocktails, particularly one made by my grandfather who tended to have a heavy hand with the whiskey. I didn't want to disappoint my grandparents, so we said we would stay for just one drink.

"Well, after only one drink, I made my excuses to leave and at the car discovered my boyfriend and I were unable, after that one drink, to lift the boat and get it back on top of the car! The drink my grandfather had made was so strong, I had to call for help, and my eighty-year-old grandfather had to come and help us! Looking back, I don't recall how we got home and am shocked that my grandfather allowed us to leave in that condition. I don't think he realized how blitzed we were!"

They all laughed spurring Caroline on to share other memories.

"There was another time that something funny happened with my brother when we were little, probably about nine or ten. My brother and I were upstairs in my grandmother's room and my brother opened a bureau drawer and found what he thought was a red M&M. My brother started to eat it but quickly realized it didn't taste like candy, running to the toilet to spit it out. Lord knows what that pill was!"

The three women laughed surmising what it could have been and created a variety of humorous outcomes. Their laughter brought levity to the evening, so much so that as they left, there were still some giggles emanating from the stairway as they descended from the loft.

A few weeks later, shortly after settling into their comfortable chairs and sampling a homemade cookie Caroline had baked for the group, they exchanged a few recipes. Beth picked up her knitting and seemed eager to begin talking.

"I know I left you all wondering what happened after I got the phone call from Jack's mother. I can tell you I suffer from a terrible sense of abandonment, but I don't know if it is because of that night or other things that happened to me that makes me feel very alone. Even saying the word 'goodbye' are too painful, so I never use them. I always just say in parting, 'See you later'. I wasn't ready a few weeks ago to keep talking about that night because it ties into that abandonment feeling. But my therapist is encouraging me to keep talking, so I want to tell you more. I'm starting to figure out with my therapist why what I did that night was influenced by what I needed emotionally."

Beth

1959

"After I hung up the phone with Jack's mother, I asked my parents to borrow one of our cars and drove to Jack's house. Jack's mother was calm but obviously concerned for me and her son's safety. We talked and she said she would call my parents and ask them to come over. I was terrified! My father, whose anger on a normal day was extreme and frightening, was now on his way to Jack's parent's home oblivious to why he was going there."

"I remember standing in Jack's mother's kitchen and watching out the back window as my father pulled into the driveway, then entered the kitchen through the back door. Jack's mother explained the situation while my father stood without a word. He told her he had a friend who was a doctor who he could call to confirm whether or not I was pregnant. My father made the call and then drove me to the doctor's office. After an examination, which you can imagine in itself was an uncomfortable experience for an unsuspecting sixteen-year-old; the doctor confirmed that I was indeed pregnant. Nothing was said on the way home. At the time I was more worried about where Jack was and his safety than what was going to happen to me."

"My Gosh, Beth, I can't even imagine how terrified I would have been," Sarah remarked empathetically. "I'm so sorry, Beth, you had to go through that," Caroline added. "Did you think your parents wanted you get an abortion?"

"Remember," Beth reminded them, "it was the late 1950's and birth control pills weren't available until the early 1960's. In the late 1950's, abortions were illegal and never even talked about. I didn't know what was going to happen to me, but with my parent's strong Christian background, I knew abortion was not one of the options they would consider, and I didn't think I could have done that anyway.

"When my father and I got home, we were barely through the door when he said, 'Go to your room and stay there until I say you can come out.' I heard my father talking to my mother in their bedroom. I could hear her crying. Then my father came into my room. 'You are not to speak to anyone. Do you understand me?', my father shouted. 'And you are not to have any contact with Jack – now or ever. Do you hear what I am saying?'" I just nodded that I heard.

"That night I lay on my bed. I was numb. I was terrified and alone. Jack had abandoned me and here I was worried about him. I had no idea what my parents were going to do or how I was going to be punished. I began to feel an invisible shield squeeze my chest. I began to withdraw; my heart and soul shrank to near nothing. My brother and sister were forbidden to speak with me. After I heard my parents come up the stairs that night and go to their room, I overheard them speaking on the phone to someone. I heard bits and pieces of the conversation; something about my going away; something about a baby; something about deciding if they wanted the baby. As I heard the conversation ending, my father said, 'Let us know after you've talked it over.'"

"Who did you think they were talking to? Didn't you think it was strange your father was on the phone talking to someone about giving away your baby?" Sarah asked incredulously.

"I didn't know so I crept slowly out of my bed and across the hall to my parent's room. I was crying hysterically. I threw myself on the floor between their twin beds, curling my knees to my chest as though that could protect my fragile heart; help me to feel safe, block the rage, and stifle the fear. I asked them 'What are you going to do to me?' Through pursed lips, my father snarled, 'We will tell you when we are good and ready and not a minute before. Go back to bed.' I pulled myself up off the floor, bent over in pain, I staggered out of their room back to the safety of my bedroom. Crawling into my bed, I pulled the blankets up to my chin and fell asleep sobbing quietly under the covers so as not to disturb my little sister sleeping in the other bed."

"Why couldn't they have realized how frightened you were and done something to help you?' Caroline asked in anger. 'Were they so insensitive to your fear that they couldn't offer any reassurance that they would help you?"

Beth lowered her head and replied, "My parents were so angry and worried about the disgrace to the family I had created, they couldn't think beyond how to solve the problem as quickly as possible, make the baby disappear and move on – no one the wiser. "

"My father had terrified me since I was a little more than two years old when I met him for the first time," Beth explained.

"You met your father for the first time when you were two? Were you adopted?" Sarah wanted to clarify.

"No, I wasn't adopted but I've always called myself a 'war baby' - not the 'great war' but World War II, because I was born during the war and that impacted my family and me.

"My mother was an only child adored by her parents. They lived in a nice home in New Jersey, not far from the shore and close to the factory where her father worked. When she was thirteen, she met the man who would become my father."

"My father went to a private high school in New Jersey and then attended Princeton University. He always knew he wanted to become an attorney. His parents owned a summer home at the Jersey shore and each June my grandfather would move the entire family to the summer house where the children could dig for clams, play in the ocean or play tennis while the grownups sat on the large screened porch overlooking the ocean playing bridge or sipping a Manhattan at dusk.

"When my mother completed high school, she went on to a two-year local community college and, after two years in a secretarial program, she was offered a position in a local law firm. My father graduated from Princeton in 1938, just a year prior to the outbreak of World War II when France and England declared war on Germany."

"While the war was raging in Europe, my father was at law school. In 1941, when the Japanese bombed Pearl Harbor and Hitler declared war on the United States, my father was in the process of completing law school and immediately enlisted in the Navy. In the spring of the following year, my mother and father were married in a quiet small ceremony attended by only their parents and immediate family just months prior to my father's deployment to the Pacific; he didn't return until the end of the war in 1945. Their wedding was filmed on old black and white film which, as young children, my siblings and I used to enjoy watching.

"As soon as my father left, my mother moved in with her parents and within only two months, she learned that she was pregnant with me. I was born in 1943 and that's why I think of myself as 'a war baby'. My mother and father wrote letters back and forth and friends offered support to my mother while her parents provided a roof over her head with a great deal of love.

"I'm told that after my birth, my father, while at watch on deck of a battleship off the coast of Casablanca, received a telegram announcing that he was indeed a father but, in the confusion to get word to him, the telegram neglected to mention if he was the father of a son or a daughter."

"How long was it before your father learned if you were a girl or a boy?" Sarah wondered.

"I'm not sure but someone told me the message was sent right away in the next telegram."

"My mother always told me how she wanted to give me her maiden name as my first name, but was hesitant to do so as she and my father had never discussed names before his deployment. She was afraid to assume her maiden name would be acceptable to my father, so she chose instead to name me after a child star, new to the screen in Hollywood… Elizabeth Taylor – obviously why I'm Beth.

"My mother sent endless photographs to my father so he was involved, at least through pictures. My mother created a thick scrapbook that's filled with sheets of notes by my mother and hundreds of pictures. If she was invited to a lunch, the invitation was glued to the scrapbook".

"Is the scrapbook still around?" Sarah asked

"Oh sure. It's kept with other family scrapbooks in a closet. I used to occasionally look through it, but haven't in years. My mother was quite a 'scrapbooker' and documented every event in the first two and a half years for my father. He missed the beginning important first years of my physical and emotional development. I think that had a big impact on my life."

"You don't have memories of those years, right?" Caroline asked.

"No, I don't remember them, but I'm convinced it made a difference. Imagine this. This man appears in my life who is a stranger. The opportunity to bond with this parent is gone. I'm sure I was quite content to be the center of attention of my mother and her doting parents; all of whom were warm and loving. I know I was adored by each of them."

"I'm not quite sure yet what you're saying, Beth."

"I think my father's absence in my beginning years, Sarah, had a huge influence on me and was behind the decision which influenced the course of my later life.

"I was told when I was older that my father's arrival created sheer panic in me and that I cried and screamed for hours as he attempted, in his unrelenting way with a lack of understanding, to show me that he was my father, and come Hell or high water, I would welcome him as my father. I think it was a power struggle between the two of us. One of my mother's friends told me years later, my father would hold me tightly on his lap as I screamed bloody murder, terrified of this stranger, until my mother would come along and rescue me."

"Remember, my mother and I were living with my grandparents but, once my father came home, they rented a house next to my grandparents and we moved there for about five years. At least I was able to see my grandparents even though we weren't living with them.

"My father began work in a law firm while my mother adjusted to a new life with a husband she hadn't seen in almost three years."

"Can you imagine what a huge adjustment that must have been for your mother? Setting up a new house, getting used to a man she hadn't seen in a long time and who she had barely lived with very long before he left, and sharing a baby that she had been raising as a single parent?"

"I'm sure it was an adjustment! Knowing my father now, I can guess he came home ready to 'reclaim' his wife from her parents, assume the role of head of the family and begin a family in earnest! I don't remember being two, but I have memories of 'life after the war'. Life was upbeat, and conversation at the table was filled with a feeling of optimism.

"I think I had begun to try and sort some things out in my mind before I even started to see a therapist, but he's helped me put feelings into words – just another observer."

"Sometimes I think I would like to see a therapist. I'm not sure everyone wouldn't benefit. Where did you find him? Did someone recommend him to you?" Caroline asked.

"No. He is actually the husband of a woman I teach with and I had met him on a few occasions but not professionally. It didn't take him long to help me see where my feelings of displacement and abandonment had come from after I shared my childhood. Things were happening pretty fast in my little world. Within a year of my father's return, my mother was pregnant and gave birth to my brother. Exactly two years after my brother's birth, I remember the morning I was sleeping at my grandparents, when my father came in, woke me up and told me I had a new baby sister named after my mother."

"How old were you at this point, Beth?"

"Sarah, I was only about five when all this was happening. I don't remember a lot during that time, but I definitely remember that morning when my father woke me up.

"Within a few years, I had been uprooted from my grandparent's home, was no longer an only child, and had a father who terrified me. Six months after my sister was born, my parents bought a house in a neighboring town distancing me further from my grandparents, the nursery school I went to and everything else I was familiar with. "

"Do you remember the move at all?"

"Funny thing, Caroline. Of course, I remember the house because I lived there until I got married. But I don't remember the move being traumatic. For some strange reason, I recall being impressed with the cafeteria line on my first day of kindergarten!"

"That's funny!" Caroline laughed.

"Our new house had three bedrooms and I shared one with my sister which I hated – especially later when I became a teenager and had this little sister hanging around in the room when my friends came over!

"The neighborhood was great though. There were a lot of kids and we were never without friends to play with. There were woods all around the house – acres, where we explored, created trails and paths – we even discovered hidden small ponds. In the winter, we cleared trails in the woods so we could go sledding. Right behind our house, we made a path which we bordered on either side with rocks. It led to 'a clubhouse' we created from scraps of discarded wood from my parent's remodeled kitchen."

"Beth, that sounds wonderful!! It sounds as though you and your friends created your own little world there," Sarah said.

"Oh, we definitely did. Near our clubhouse was a huge hole in the earth where years before a builder had unsuccessfully attempted to blast a foundation for a new house. For some reason, the builder abandoned the project which left a huge deep hole lined with big boulders. It resembled a large canyon and we named it that. Sometimes we would spend an entire day playing imagining games at the 'canyon'. We climbed up and down the boulders pretending we were cowboys in the wild west like The Lone Ranger and Hopalong Cassidy, our favorite TV idols."

"I'm surprised your parents let you play there. Wasn't it dangerous, Beth?" Caroline asked.

"I am too. Yeah, it was very dangerous. If one of those boulders had dislodged, it could have caused a major landslide! That was how we spent our summer days though. If we weren't hanging out in our 'clubhouse', we were playing 'Cowboys and Indians' at the canyon. At night after supper, we played kickball in the front yard with all the kids. Sometimes, my father came out and played with us which made it even more fun."

"I'm glad you have some happy memories, Beth. I'm thankful that I have my happy memories of the weekends with my grandparents to hold onto." Sarah commented.

"I agree. Outside my family, things were wonderful. But life seemed to be moving faster than I could keep up with. Sometimes I look back and can see now that I was beginning to lose ground with this new family. You know how people say, 'a picture is worth a thousand words' and speaks volumes? Well, there are two photographs which come to mind. Both are telling in my mind. One of the first photographs was taken when I was about five. My father and I are on the front lawn of his parent's summer home and my father is kneeling on one knee, resting his arm on his knee. I am standing nearby with my hands clasped behind my back."

"What do you think that picture means, Beth?"

"In my mind, Sarah, clearly I see a man and a child. There is no physical contact; we are just a man and a child who happened to be captured in the same picture. There is no visible connection. There's a second picture. It was the first family photograph in our new house. Whenever I look at the picture, even today, the same feeling comes back to me. I see a picture that represents how I identified my place within the family. In this picture, my parents are seated beside each other in armchairs. My brother is seated on the arm of my mother's chair while my sister is sitting on the arm of my father's chair. The four are clustered together. I am standing behind the chair, still in the picture but only on the edge. When I look at that picture, I see 'them' and then there is 'me'. When I look at that picture, I see my brother and sisters who look alike and resemble my father while I don't look like them. I resemble my mother's side of the family. Even their names! My brother is named after my father and my sister was given my mother's name. I'm the odd one out."

"Do your brother and sisters know you feel this way?"

"I doubt it, Caroline. We've never really talked about it. But my brother and sister and I are very different, I think. Both of them are much more outgoing and exuberant than I am. I think they're more self-assured.

"My therapist has helped me to see that it's not surprising that I feel this way and that my personality and my siblings are different. The bottom line is my siblings and I were raised by a different set of adults. The first two plus important developmental years of my life were spent without my father. The adults present in my life were my mother and her parents. My brother and sister, on the other hand, spent their first two important years with my parents; two adults who were essentially starting, for a second time, married life after the interruption of the war. My parents faced enormous challenges of assimilating into a post war world, with a new home and now three children. My siblings were raised initially by my parents whereas I was not.

Sarah and Caroline were scowling in their attempt to understand the complexities of what Beth was describing.

For clarification, Sarah reiterated, "So I think I understand what you're saying. During the first two or three years of your life, developmentally extremely important years for establishing your personality, securities and environmental influences, you were raised by your mother, your grandfather and your grandmother. After your father's return, he and your mother were the primary adults in the beginning developmental years for your siblings. That makes sense."

"Yes. I know my mother was a different person with her parents than how she was with my father, who she had barely lived with for any length of time after their marriage. I'll explain what I mean.

"Even when I was little, I remember that adults were excited about the future; dinner table talk was enthusiastic with planning for a bright future. The purchase of a washing machine was a big thing. The attitude was the war was over; we had won; the future was bright. Everyone was ready to get on with life. My father had a good job and although frugal, we lived in a very comfortable suburban home.

"I liked my new school and feel that my desire to become a teacher was due to the warm and welcoming environment of my elementary school and the teachers I had in the primary grades. I have warm memories of helping my first- grade teacher by mixing easel paints and helping my second- grade teacher straighten up her classroom at the end of the day. I am able to recall learning cursive writing in third grade, using an inkwell and pen for the first time and even a few of the stories we read in third grade. I admit they're not earth- shattering memories but I like to think of them because it reassures me that there were some positive things in my childhood.

"My parents had so many friends. There was always some social event at our house or their friend's. They belonged to a bowling group which met one night weekly, they belonged to a tennis group on weekends, a bridge group one or two nights a month, a community theater group and an indoor badminton league two nights a week. They were constantly with friends."

"It sounds as though your parents weren't home a lot. Did your mother work?"

"Are you kidding, Sarah? My father was of the old-fashioned mind that a woman's place was in the home and didn't allow my mother to work. So, she was a Brownie leader to a group of girls my sister's age and volunteered at the hospital gift shop one day a week.

"When I was in fifth grade, my father and mother shared lead roles in an amateur community group in a play called 'Only an Orphan Girl'. It was one of those stories that had a villain with a handlebar mustache, a top hat and black cape standing over the lumber mill's large table saw; the heroine was strapped to the moving belt when the hero bursts into the room to save her. I wasn't the orphan girl but played another character and felt quite important on stage enjoying the sound of enthusiastic applause when I took my final bow. My theatrical debut may have helped me later!

"One morning when I was sitting at my desk in sixth grade, my teacher introduced a new student to the class and placed her in a desk beside mine. She asked me to be her friend and help her become acquainted. Her name was Jane. I can still recall that day and we've remained friends over the years. I didn't know at that time that Jane would become my savior five years later. My parents did not like her. They felt she was a bad influence on me because her parents gave her a lot of freedom whereas I had little!

"By the time I was thirteen, I was doing everything I could to get out of the house. When I was young, we played outside all the time as I said, but when I became a teenager, that wasn't what I wanted to do. My parents were strict about my being able to go out with friends and even asking a friend over. If Jane came over, we would go to my room and try to have some privacy like all teenagers need, but since I shared my room with my younger sister, she usually made a point of hanging out with us so we couldn't talk about the kinds of things teenagers talk about. Instead of inviting friends over, I escaped emotionally and mentally by remaining in my room where I would lie on my bed and gaze out the window imaging all sorts of creative faces and creatures in the leaves of the trees outside.

"Just like many adults, my happiest memories when I was a teenager were those times spent with my friends. I often spent weekends at Jane's house, because she had freedom and we were actually able to meet up with our friends. As soon as she turned sixteen, Jane got her driver's license and could take the family car on weekends and evenings. Suddenly not only did she have more freedom, but I did too! Even though my parents didn't like her, I didn't care. Jane and I became fast friends and still are after thirty years. When we're visiting, which doesn't happen often because she lives a distance away, we talk about the past. Jane often talks about what I was like as a teenager and I find her comments very interesting. She brings my teenage years into focus through another set of eyes because she was there to witness those years with me.

"I was always envious of Jane's relationship with her father. He was fun and actually enjoyed hearing about our friends and our antics; something that my father had shown little interest in. I remember the first time I heard the name Elvis Presley and saw his picture on the front of a record album Jane's father bought her. I clearly remember the night The Beatles performed on the Ed Sullivan Show where my father was not shy in expressing his horror about this new kind of music. Of course, I thought Elvis Presley and Paul McCartney were 'dreamy' but this new style of music enjoyed by teenagers was appalling to my father. He liked classical music and the big band sound of Glenn Miller. It took much pleading from the back seat to get him to put 'our music' on the car radio."

Caroline laughed. "Isn't it funny looking back and recalling how our parents reacted to the music and antics of Elvis Presley? I think of my father's reaction to our music every time I hear some of the music our kids listen to today. I guess it's no different. Isn't it true that Socrates was supposed to have questioned, 'What's wrong with kids today?' They all giggled.

"My father was not only a prominent attorney but well-known and highly respected in the community. He was chairman of a number of professional organizations so his reputation was important. My mother, for whatever reason, was always concerned about 'What will people think?'. It was always about the image and that I had brought shame to the family being pregnant. In her mind, it was extremely important that we were thought of in the community as an upstanding family. When my sister or I went out on a date, my mother told us, 'You are not to sit in the driveway when you are coming home from a date. What would people think?'

"I know my parents sent my brother and me to private schools in part because deep down they wanted to give us the best opportunity for success, but private school also sent a message of success, I think. We were supposed to portray to the public that we were a close family. Even years later, friends of my parents would comment on what wonderful parents I had, how fortunate I was, what a terrific family I was a part of. Looking back, in reality, they were probably right in part. My siblings and I were secure knowing, perhaps subconsciously, that my successful father could provide for us. His success became my security but couldn't make up for his inability to convey affection or connect with me emotionally.

"Since the moment the doctor had confirmed my pregnancy the day before, my parents spoke very little to me. I was being punished. When my father drove me to school that Monday morning after being called to Jack's home, we rode in silence. I sat close to the door, trying to stay as far away as possible both physically and emotionally. It was so uncomfortable. What could I say? 'I'm sorry' didn't seem appropriate or enough. I sat in the passenger seat wanting to crawl out of my skin. Even though I was wrapped in a self-imposed cocoon, I didn't feel safe.

"At the end of the day, I was called into my parent's room. My father said, 'You are to call every one of your friends as I stand here. You are to tell every friend that you and your mother are not getting along and you fight all the time. You are to tell them that you are going to go live in Illinois with a friend of the family because your parents decided it would be best if you were separated for a while.' One by one, I made the calls. Maybe, it was the theatrical experience I had learned a years ago when I acted in the play, 'Only an Orphan Girl', which helped me to give a convincing performance. I could tell as I hung up the phone from the last call, my parents felt assured the first step of their plan had been put into action. I was on auto pilot."

"Did you even know at that point, Beth, what was going to happen?"

"No, I just knew I was going to Illinois but I didn't know anything else, Sarah. My father hadn't told me anything and my mother never said a word. The fear I had felt toward my father, that began when he returned home from the war, was still with me. It is beyond my comprehension that, despite that fear, I would challenge his anger by disobeying his orders. But I did. The first time I was alone, I called Jane and told her the truth."

"I can't believe you did that either. You were still a rebel! I'm afraid to think what your father would have done if he had found out."

'I don't know, Sarah, but he never found out. I needed someone and Jane was there for me'.

"Jane became my support system, my communication with my world of friends, my pipeline for information. She connected me with Jack's sister who called me almost every day and told me if Jack had been found or if anyone had heard from him. Jane became my ally and voice at the high school when an update announcement was made about the missing student or when another student snickered about Jack having run away, mocking. Jane took them on one by one."

"Did they let you see any of your friends or were you grounded?" Sarah asked.

"Well it wasn't as though they were going to let me go to parties, but they did allow me one last sleepover at Jane's house before I would be going away. I cried that night sitting at their kitchen table with her mother, looking for assurances. I desperately wanted Jane's mother to tell me that everything would all be all right. I begged her to tell me that Jack was all right and that of course, Jack and I would be together some day. I needed hope more than I needed anything else. Without hope, all I had was me. Her mother could offer no assurance.

"Remember, it was December. It was the holiday season. Everyone was excited about the break from school and the holiday. I felt none of it."

"Had your parents told you yet where you were going? I can't believe you went this long without knowing what was going to happen. It almost seems like they were making you pay for what you had done."

"I don't know. Maybe you're right, Caroline. It wasn't as though I could ask. I knew from what they told me to tell my friends that I would be living in Illinois with friends of my parents but I had no idea who these people were because I had never met them. It turned out it was a friend of my mother's she had met in college and who was her friend when my father was in the war. They eventually told me these people lived in an apartment and agreed to take me in and I would be staying with them until it was over. They never said what 'it' was, but I knew. We never uttered the word 'pregnant'. I was told my parents would be taking me there immediately after the holidays."

"Did you just keep going to school in November and through Christmas as though nothing was different?" Sarah asked.

"I know I continued through November and probably the first part of December, but being a private school, I think our holiday break was longer and started earlier than the public high school. I recall just going through the motions. I had shut down and moved through each day as though in a trance. I was ashamed and embarrassed. I'm sure none of my classmates knew I wasn't returning to school after the holiday break, but I suspect the faculty knew since my father must have told them. I don't recall ever even saying goodbye to any of them on the last day before break.

"On the last night before I left for Illinois, my mother made a big dinner which we ate in the dining room. It was supposed to be a special night as I was going to go to Illinois, which according to 'the story' my parents had created, my mother and I were not getting along and we needed to be separated. Everyone was relieved that 'calm' would be restored in the family and therefore it was something to celebrate, too special to be celebrated in the kitchen where we usually ate. My mother prepared one of her special meals, Yankee pot roast with potatoes and carrots. My grandfather, who now lived with us, sat beside me at the table. Since I had spent the first five years of my life living in a house beside his and he having raised me in those first few years, I think I was my grandfather's favorite grandchild. I didn't realize, until decades later, how he must have grieved to know that his favorite granddaughter was going away for a while and would be out of his reach. I learned later how much he had missed me.

"The meal was pretty solemn despite the fact that my parents attempted to make it seem like a joyous occasion. The tension was thick in the air and conversation was strained. When my fifteen-year-old brother said 'I guess this is like The Last Supper', my mother threw down her napkin and ran crying from the table. We all looked at each other in shock. No one said anything but my brother knew that he had said something wrong. He just didn't have any idea what that might be. Later my mother came to my room and cried. 'This would kill your grandfather if he knew!' I was sixteen and filled with tremendous embarrassment, shame and guilt – always the guilt! I didn't know then it would take over thirty years to overcome the damage one night had caused."

"Did your grandfather seem upset when you left?" Caroline asked.

"As I recall, he gave me a hug and said he would see me soon. I don't remember, Caroline that he was visibly sad but I'm sure he probably was. He never struck me as an emotional man just a kind and gentle man. Maybe he even guessed the truth. He wasn't stupid. I don't know if he ever really found out for sure."

"In January we began the train trip west which took two days. It should have felt interminable but it didn't because I didn't care. I didn't care if it took a lifetime to get there. I didn't know anyone there, was going to be without friends, abandoned by my parents and taken from all that was familiar. So, what if the trees were just a blur? So, what if my parents had barely spoken to me for days? So, what if I had been emotionally ostracized from my family within hours of my parents finding out about my 'indiscretion'? So, what if I could intellectually justify what I had done because, for the first time in my life, there was someone who was able to demonstrate love and affection to me, proving I was a lovable human being? The plain and simple truth was that my parents had never been emotionally available to me and I was three months pregnant, carrying a baby conceived one night in a show of passion and love with Jack, a night which would influence a large part of my life.

"I know I was supposed to feel humiliated by the shame I had brought upon my family, but I didn't. That came later. I know I was supposed to feel remorse, but I was too scared. I just remember sitting and doing what I was told. I had shut down. I had withdrawn into a world which I only allowed Jane to share. I had no one. I had two days to emotionally prepare for how to deal with living with people I didn't know, let alone being pregnant which I knew little about. I knew I could cope but hadn't had enough time to figure it all out. I just knew deep- down, that I needed to build an inner strength and make sure no one could hurt me again. The shield I had already started to build would protect me. I just had to figure out how to keep my fears and feelings hidden from the world. It never occurred to me that at some time in the future, I would find it safe to allow someone past the shield, choose to forgive Jack for leaving me, forgive my parents for their inability to give me the kind of love I needed or even forgive myself.

"Even though my parents were physically on the train, I was alone. Jack was not there. He was gone and was the person I thought I needed most for my emotional support. All I had of Jack was simply a note he had left for his mother as to why he was leaving and the baby I was carrying."

When Beth finished, not a sound could be heard in the room; Sarah and Caroline were speechless. Even the needles were silent. Remnants of knitted yarn lay on Caroline and Sarah's lap as the two had become so absorbed in the unfolding of Beth's journey, that their hands had ceased moving.

Crying, Caroline spoke. "I'm angry, Beth, and I don't even know your parents."

"I feel the same way, Sarah. My heart aches for you and your pain. Now that we're mothers, can you imagine, if that had been your daughter, how differently we would have handled it."

Caroline and Sarah reached out to Beth and enclosed her in a three-way embrace. During the week, the three women spoke by phone supporting each other with the difficult revelations each had made.

Over the following weeks and months, the journeys of each women unraveled.

Sarah was anxious to announce an exciting bit of news that had developed unexpectantly.

"I know you both know how much I love to decorate, but since the day I moved into our house, I never felt it offered the warmth I always wanted no matter how hard I tried to make it inviting. I didn't like that the ceilings are so high and the rooms too large. Well, Rick came home last night and said there's a small, early 18thC house for sale in town and he thought we should look at it. We're going Saturday. I can't wait! Even better, it has a pond."

Caroline waited and didn't want to detract from exciting chatter of a new home. But when the conversation reached a lull, Caroline used the fact that Sarah talked of the warmth of a home, to direct the conversation back to the night she had driven to the hospital. She was hoping Beth and Sarah's perspective would bring her some comfort.

"Sarah, I know exactly what you mean about how a woman feels about her home. I know how important it is to feel that your home is warm and it brings comfort. When I told you about the night Steve went wild and damaged our home. I was livid. I had worked so hard to create a home that was warm and homey. I took it personally and felt his actions violated me. I was scared but furious. I didn't know if I wanted to drive to the hospital. I didn't know if I ever wanted to see him again and have him enter our house. But listening to you both over the past weeks and months, it just seems as though there are similarities in our lives and if anyone would understand, you both will.

"I know you know that Steve isn't my first husband. My first husband, Bill, and I were childhood sweethearts and throughout our teen years never considered dating anyone else. We were pretty comfortable with each other and had basically grown up together. My parents liked Bill and his family as we lived in the same neighborhood and our parents saw each other socially. We shared a common history and knew the same people so it was a very comfortable relationship.

"Bill was tall, nice-looking with a boyish face, and smart. I really liked his family, especially his father who was a warm and loving man with a beaming smile and infectious laugh. I feel as though he and I bonded on the first night when I was invited to dinner at Bill's house. I was a nervous wreck sitting at the table with Bill, his parents and his brother, and tried to make conversation. I don't recall what was on my plate other than a pile of peas, but during the conversation, my knife slipped as I cut my meat and peas sprayed across the table, most of them ended up near Bill's father's plate. I was mortified, but his dad chuckled and made a funny comment, that smoothed over my embarrassment. He was endearing and I think we connected from that point on."

Sarah and Beth both giggled at the image of everyone at the table getting out of the way of flying peas.

"Bill's father seemed so different than mine. In my family, there was an expectation, particularly by my father, that my brother, sisters and I were going to be successful. I'm not sure it was even verbalized directly but there were unspoken messages from my father with his reaction to my grades, interests, talents, friends and achievements. He had little tolerance for less than the best we could do. Since I was the oldest, the message I heard was no matter what I did, it wasn't good enough. I never heard the words, 'Good for you', 'I'm proud of you', 'Great job', or 'Good girl'.

"I was always told I could do better, and looking back I can see where many of the decisions I made in life were based on my trying to win praise from my father and prove to him that I was worthy. I know even today I keep wanting to move into a bigger house than the one we lived in, thinking maybe my father would see me as successful - and then he would love me. I'm beginning to piece together how many times I felt I was judged and loved based on what I accomplished not on who I was. I went back to school to finish my degree, and I'm glad, because I thought then my father would be proud of me. My father liked Bill and

I think in the back of my mind, I knew I loved him but I wonder if I subconsciously thought if I married Bill, the man my father liked, then he would love me. Then my father would be proud of me. Then I would hear the words from him that I wanted….'Good job'….'Good girl'."

"I'm sure your father loved you, Caroline. I don't think you should doubt that."

"I know in hindsight, Sarah, in my heart my father loved me in 'his way'; just not the way I needed to know and feel that I was loved for who I was, not what I did."

"I can relate to that," mumbled Beth, a bit under her breath, as she too had experienced some of the same needs for physical affection in her past.

"Bill and I attended local universities and we got married right after graduation. Our marriage was never a question of 'if' but 'when'. Without doubt, Bill and I married with the expectation, as each bride and groom does, that we were so compatible, we would of course live happily ever after. We wanted to have a small, quiet ceremony at the country club in town, nothing fancy, and after the ceremony left for a brief honeymoon at a country inn a few hours away in a quaint New England village.

"We were so naïve! Here we were in our early twenties, and thought we were so grown-up enough to handle marriage and all that it entailed. In the early 1950s, it was pretty common for couples to marry young. Can you imagine today kids marrying when they've just turned twenty? Now, young people want to stay single longer and enjoy life before settling down. We had very little money even though Bill's position as an insurance adjuster paid a good salary, but was still an entry level wage. and my job as a first-year teacher paid just over seven thousand dollars. It never occurred to us that we couldn't make it. We were the classic example of 'love is blind'.

"In addition to wedding gifts from family and friends like household pots and pans, serving utensils and towels, many of our friends and family gave us money which totaled a little more than twelve hundred dollars. I remember thinking, 'Wow! Twelve hundred dollars!'- a fortune. We carefully shopped for a box spring and mattress knowing we couldn't afford a bed with a headboard. We had money enough for a metal frame. We searched and bought a fifteen- year old car for fifty dollars which looked as though it was left over from the Second World War! We bought a twin mattress and frame that we converted to a couch, an armchair and a television so small it was barely visible from across the room. Our kitchen table was a folding card table. We were so proud of how we had used our wedding funds and thought we had everything we needed to begin our life of wedded bliss.

"We looked at a lot of apartments but found out pretty quickly that we couldn't afford most of them. We were looking in a fairly large New England city and found a newly constructed apartment building on a quiet side street not far from Bills' office. We looked at an apartment on the first floor but found we couldn't afford the rent on any of the above- ground units. The agent, anxious to make a sale, showed us a basement unit we could afford. Because it was below ground, the windows, similar in style to basement windows, were located high on the walls at ceiling level, permitting little light to any room. That didn't matter to either of us and we immediately signed the lease, proud of our success and feeling we were home at last. It wasn't until we had moved in, we realized that the water, alongside the driveway leading to the parking lot behind the building, sometimes pooled on the pavement when it rained. Later we laughed as we lay in bed on a rainy night as a car traveling to the parking lot would plow through the pooled water above our heads making it sound as though we were about to be splashed and soaked. We were too enamored with our new beginning of wedded bliss to think of this apartment as anything less than perfect. It was home.

"Over the first few months, we were able to afford a few more things for our apartment; rugs, more lamps, two small bureaus – even an old ringer washing machine on wheels that I kept tucked in the kitchen corner and pulled to the sink when needed. We existed on cheap meals! We ate a lot of hot dogs and fish which back then cost very little. Pancakes were not only quick to make but dirt cheap. I came up with ways to 'dress up' a can of spam with brown sugar, dotted with whole cloves, which I proudly referred to as a roast. Even a box of Kleenex was a luxury we couldn't afford."

Sarah laughed recalled some of the meals she had served her family when she was first married.

"I found more ways to disguise a pound of ground beef into different meals than Julia Childs could have imagined. I think I could have written a best-seller cookbook on the use of hamburger! I made something called Swedish meatballs which were nothing more than hamburger balls with a can of cream of mushroom soup, not to be confused with something the kids called 'squish', hamburger with diced tomatoes and macaroni."

Beth added, "Don't forget ground beef meatloaf with chopped olives and tomato sauce on top or my kids' favorite, meatloaf with pieces of buttered bread crumbs on top."

"We were married only six months when I learned I was pregnant. Of course, we were excited but never stopped to think how this was going to change our lives not to mention the loss of income. I had an easy pregnancy. With the addition of our baby, the apartment suddenly seemed very small, and we moved to a two-family suburban house where we rented what seemed like a mansion because it had two bedrooms. We stayed there for four years and then with three children, found a very small ranch-style project home just down the street from the apartment. The down payment was only five-hundred dollars which we borrowed from Bill's parents."

"Can you imagine needing a down payment of only five-hundred dollars to buy a house?" Beth joked.

"Bill had been promoted a few times over the years and on the surface, we appeared to the outside world to be a happy family. We discovered later each of us was saddened by a marriage which never materialized into the dream we envisioned. I returned to teaching when the kids started school so that kept me busy while Bill was putting in long hours climbing the ladder at work. We were involved actively in our children's activities with sports and scouting, often moving to a bigger house and decorating another home. Just like you mentioned Sarah that you didn't feel your big house felt like home, I think I kept moving looking for the house that would feel like home. I was looking for warmth and loving surroundings, unaware that the size of a house doesn't create a feeling of a home. As the children grew, we also moved to accommodate our growing family, and we were always mindful to live in a nice neighborhood for the children and a town with a good school system.

We looked at each other eight years ago and realized that at the end of all those years of marriage, we had focused so much on our children and trying to make ends meet, that we had given nothing to our marriage. We had grown so far apart emotionally, neither one of us could give the other what they needed. We decided we both wanted a more loving relationship and decided to get a divorce. It was very hard. I cried a lot because I felt so sad for Bill knowing he was a good man and I had hurt him.

"Bill and I are close and are both involved in our children's lives. We do our best to make everything as comfortable for the kids as we can. Bill spends a lot of time with the kids even though they live with me. He has been dating someone whom I suspect he will eventually marry and I'm glad to see he seems happy. That helps a little with my feeling of guilt because I always question if I could have done something differently that would have resulted in a better outcome."

"It's nice that you can have that amicable relationship with your ex-husband, Caroline. You're lucky," Beth commented.

"Remember when I told you when we first met that a publishing company had offered me a job as a sales rep in the New England area? I've been stalling because I've been afraid to commit to it even though the salary would be four times what I make as a teacher. It's tempting but I've wanted to be a teacher since the time I was a kid and I'm afraid to give up my teaching position. I'm not sure I could return to the classroom if I found I missed teaching or this new job turned out to be something other than what I wanted. Well, I applied for a leave of absence and found out last night that my request was denied by the Board of Education, so this morning I submitted my letter of resignation at the end of the school year."

"Congratulations, Caroline. That's great news!!! I bet you'll end up loving it and you might find it will be easier than teaching the special education children. You'll get to work with adults for a change," Sarah said enthusiastically.

Beth was concerned when she thought about Steve's past behavior. "What does Steve think about your new job, Caroline? Does he realize your hours are going to be different if you're traveling around the state and you might be spending less time at home?"

"That was one reason I hesitated taking the job in the first place. Then the more I thought about it, I decided I have to do what makes me happy. He will have to deal with my being late occasionally and get over it. I'm hopeful that now that he's not drinking, he can face up to some of his insecurities and we won't have any incidents like we had before."

"Where did you and Steve meet?" Beth asked.

"We met at a party five years ago. I had been divorced almost three years, didn't really date much. I focused on my job and kids and read a lot or knit in my spare time. One of the women I taught with invited me to the party. I went more out of a sense of obligation than something I really wanted to do that Saturday night. I greeted everyone and was making the rounds when I was introduced to Steve. He wasn't that tall but was slender. He was dressed in a navy-blue sports jacket, white and blue striped button-down collared shirt and jeans. He had brown hair combed loosely to the side, an attractive groomed mustache, angular chin and nose. He looked pretty sharp I have to say – maybe even a little like Clark Gable."

"I think I can guess where this is going," Beth teased.

"Steve was the epitome of an extrovert; high energy, outgoing, quick to smile - his infectious laugh always ready to have a good time. He shook my hand as we were being introduced and placed his left hand on my arm, guiding me away from the source of the music so we could hear each other. I noticed his manicured nails and gold bracelet and thought to myself, 'This is a man who is concerned with his appearance, is fun and seems ready to have a good time and enjoy life.

"Wouldn't you agree from stories I've told you, that I'm pretty outgoing? I don't have a problem going up to someone to initiate a conversation. Right? Well, as we began to talk, I was looking at a man who was so engaging, I felt overshadowed by his energy and outgoing personality. It quieted me. I didn't have to struggle for conversation and listened with peaked interest as he carried the conversation. I found myself quieted by his personality and enchanted by his charm. The music was so loud it was impossible to hear what Steve was saying. Within minutes, Steve shrugged his shoulders in frustration, took my hand and pulled me toward him, motioned to the dance area, and with hand signals asked if I wanted to dance."

"Was he a good dancer?" Beth asked.

"He was great! I always loved to dance and had taken dance lessons for years but had never found a man who was a good dancer, other than my father. I was excited to discover he was a terrific dancer and we spent a good part of the evening on the dance floor. I had a great time at the party and by the end of the night realized I had not spoken to another person after having been introduced to Steve. At the end of the evening, Steve asked for my phone number and assured me he would call."

"Well, obviously he did", noted Beth.

"I was confident I would hear from him within a day or two, but it was a full week before he called. We talked about nothing earth shattering for a few minutes before he asked me if I wanted to meet for a drink after work. Steve lived in an apartment on the eastern Connecticut shore and was familiar with a seaside restaurant overlooking the harbor, and suggested we meet there. I agreed and we met in the lounge where we enjoyed continuing the conversation from the party, and sharing a bit of our past; our divorces, our careers, children and interests. A few hours passed quickly and I was beginning to feel hungry but thought I shouldn't be pushy and suggest he buy me dinner!"

"Didn't he suggest you eat? I thought you were at a restaurant."

"Yes, we were, Sarah, but we were sitting in the lounge area and he was talking so much, I think he lost track of time. He told me how he had lived by the sea for years and, having grown up working with his dad in the marine business, it was no surprise that Steve's passion was sailing. All of this information painted a picture of a man who was not only handsome in a dashing way, but fascinating to a country girl whose life seemed to pale in comparison to the adventurous experiences this man shared. By the end of the evening, I was intrigued. I was leading with my heart not my head but didn't recognize the difference at the time."

"Isn't it ironical that each of us thought we knew what we wanted with a partner and have been forced to look at why.? At least Caroline and I did," Beth mentioned quietly, seemingly thinking aloud.

"It sounds to me that we were all looking for something we needed which we didn't get when we were younger. I don't think you should be so hard on yourself, Caroline, or feel ashamed for making the choice you did. Look at my life," Beth added.

Caroline nodded in agreement. Beth continued, "Just listening to you talk about your father, Caroline, and his inability to express emotions, particularly about showing affection, strikes such a familiar chord with how I described my father and the parallels between the two fathers.

"It's pretty amazing isn't it, that daughters are so greatly affected by how their fathers treat them? We were both looking for someone to fill the emotional void our fathers left", Beth commented. She continued to offer another insight. "I don't think it was because our father didn't love us. Maybe back then, it was perceived as a sign of weakness if a man showed his emotion. You and I each were looking for a feeling of warmth and affection from our father which neither one of our fathers was able to give. Look where it got us! We made a choice based on what we thought was a feeling of love and affection from a man. Neither one of us was able to identify what affection felt like because we had no basis of comparison."

Caroline sat with a look of surprise on her face as pieces of a puzzle were beginning to fit. "That makes a lot of sense, Beth. I think it's true that a daughter is greatly influenced by her father, sometimes marrying a man she thinks will fill the void or marries someone like her father because it feels comfortable. I think the same thing holds true of how men are influenced by their mothers," Caroline suggested.

"My father was not his mother's favorite child and I think that contributed to how my father led his life; what he determined was essential to earn love and affection from his mother. My father made it a point to excel at everything he did – he was what we today would call 'an overachiever', to prove to his mother that he indeed was worthy of his mother's love and attention. Looking back, I suspect my father thought with each additional accomplishment, his mother would find him the more successful son; worthy of her love. I'm not sure my father won that battle, but I think it was the basis for his thinking that love was based on what you accomplished, not on who you were."

"Look where all that has gotten us." Sarah laughed.

"Caroline and her husband are in bed feeling as though they're getting soaked with water from the driveway, Beth is dressing up a can of Spam and trying to pass it off as a roast. And as I listen to you talking about how a father influences a daughter, I think the same is true between mothers and sons. My husband Rick's mother was a very strong, independent woman and I think that's one reason why Rick was drawn to me as he saw me as someone who was not independent and needed to be taken care of.

"This whole conversation makes me think about that night I told you about at my grandparent's dinner table when we were kidding my father and it turned into a scene. I know my father was trying to make my mother feel better when he ran upstairs but I don't think he was capable of emotionally making it any different for her. I suspect he was probably as emotionally unavailable to my mother as he was to us, yet, for some reason, could be charming to other women which must have made my mother envious and hurt. Let me finish telling you about that night.

"Remember I told you how my mother left the table at my grandparent's house after we teased my father about walking the lady to her car after church? Well, it was a quiet half-hour ride home. My siblings and I huddled in the backseat feeling guilty about creating this problem between our parents and unsure whether or not we would be punished when we reached home. It was late when we got home and we were told to get into bed. Our parent's bedroom was across the stairway from my sister's and mine but close enough that, as I lay in bed that night, I could hear my mother and father arguing in their bedroom. I felt sad for my mother who was crying. I heard her threatening to leave my father and tell him she wanted a divorce. Being a young kid, I listened carefully to each word without any knowledge of what repercussions their conversation had on me. However, it passed through my mind that divorce meant you didn't live with both parents but just one. I decided then if I had a choice, so strong was my need for his attention, I would go live with my father perhaps as an only child. But they never divorced. My siblings and I however learned a valuable lesson that night. We never again mentioned any instance of my father opening a car door for any woman or speaking to anyone in the parking lot at church.

"Looking back, I've wondered if that wasn't a turning point in my parent's relationship. My father was a handsome and charming man. He had a very outgoing personality and I can see why our teasing him brought pain to my mother. I see my father almost flirting with other women, but reserved with my mother, showing little or no affection despite the fact that I know he loved her very much."

"Their lack of affection was visible to us children. There was a dutiful kiss at bedtime, when my siblings and I left for school or when my father left to go to work. I never again heard my father call my Mother 'Muzzy'. There seemed to be little joy or laughter in the house. It was a serious home and I, being somewhat more sensitive than my siblings, felt the tension in the air. We spent afternoons escaping to the outdoors, playing with our friends and coming inside only when we were called for dinner. I continued to look forward to my visits to my grandparent's home where I felt safe and loved; a place which came along with laughter.

"It is no wonder that spending almost every weekend with my grandparents I developed a deep sense of love for them and dependence on them. When I was in fifth grade, just nine years old, I was given the starring role in a play being performed by my class. At the end of the performance, I took a bow and the principal of the school handed me a small bouquet of flowers. I was so overwhelmed by the accolades and what those flowers represented; I kept them in the refrigerator so they wouldn't die. Isn't that pathetic? Those flowers represented a sense of such strong recognition, something I was not accustomed to, I wanted to sustain the life of that bouquet and savor the symbolic sense of pride and accomplishment. That's pretty sad, isn't it?"

"A few days later, my grandmother had a stroke."

"Oh, I'm so sorry, Sarah. You must have been devastated," Caroline said.

"I was too young to understand what a stroke was or question why she wasn't brought to a hospital, but instead stayed at home bedridden. My mother thought seeing me would cheer up my grandmother and suggested I bring her the bouquet of flowers I had been given. I was so selfish; those flowers represented an acknowledgement of recognition I so needed. I didn't want to give them away no matter how much I loved my grandmother. I left them in the refrigerator", sobbed Sarah.

"What did you end up doing, Sarah?" Beth wanted to know.

"I went out in the yard and picked a bouquet of weeds.

"My mother warned me that, 'Grammy doesn't look like she always does.' She told me Grammy couldn't move but I could give her a hug anyway. She would like to get a hug my mother told me. She suggested I tell my grandmother about school and the school play, but warned me that my Grammy couldn't speak. To a nine-year-old, this was frightening, but I didn't want to disappoint my mother and certainly not my grandmother."

"I remember walking up the stairs and into my grand-parent's large bedroom. My grandmother looked as my mother had described. Her bed was to the left as I walked in, with windows overlooking the Sound straight ahead; but the windows had been covered. The room was dark. I did what I was told. I walked over, reached up and gave my grandmother a hug then stood beside her bed. I loved my grandmother and found it too painful to look at her. With my head down, I chattered on about school. I was too young to understand how serious the situation was. It was the last time I would see her."

Sarah began to sob and realized she was joined by Beth and Caroline who had tears running down their cheeks.

"A few mornings later, my father awakened me on a school day morning but told me I wouldn't be going to school that day. He told me that my grandmother had gone to Heaven and our babysitter would be coming soon to stay with us for the day. My father said, 'Mommy is very sad and is crying. She wants to be alone in her room so you are not to bother her.' I was devastated. I didn't understand about death but knew it meant I would never see my grandmother again. My grandmother was the first person I had loved and lost but would not be the last.

"As much as the babysitter tried to tell me my Grammy was happy in Heaven, I couldn't get past my sadness or my guilt. I was inconsolable that I had not brought my flowers to my grandmother. I hated myself for my selfishness. I was in pain, afraid that my grandmother had died thinking I didn't love her because I hadn't brought her my bouquet. I was too young and upset to figure out my grandmother would not have known about the bouquet. I would have given anything to be given a second chance. I felt a huge loss, an emptiness that I couldn't put into words. I kept asking the babysitter for assurance that I would see my grandmother again. I was too young to know anything about faith or God's will.

"For the next few months, my grandfather went into a deep depression and shut himself away from the world and us for months. Gone forever were the weekends spent at my grandparents where I had grown dependent on the love they gave. Gone was my loving grandmother, silver beads, homemade pancakes, fabric scraps and Japanese beetles. Gone was grandfather, grief-stricken and in seclusion. Gone was my safe place. I grieved the loss of it all.

"Quite a while later, I dreamed my grandmother came to visit. She gave me one of her warm hugs like the ones I always remembered. In my dream she said, 'I know you were alone as a little girl and I wish I could have been there more for you. I would always hold you close and help you to be safe. Whenever you feel afraid, just pretend that you are standing in my beautiful rose garden surrounded by my beautiful flowers.' Then she smiled at me in the dream and said, 'I smile every time I think about how you loved the beautiful buttons I collected and the antique jewelry I know you will someday wear. Remember the other beautiful flowers we grew together in our garden.' And then in my dream, her last words to me were, 'I am happy now. I want you to be happy and I will know you are when I see your smile which I have loved since you were a baby.'

"I woke up in the morning and instantly felt sad when I realized it was only a dream, but I felt a sense of peace knowing that my grandmother was alright, safe, and no longer in pain. She liked it when I smiled and so I decided I would try to smile whenever I could."

Sarah had dissolved into gulping sobs.

Caroline tried to offer words of hope. "Sarah, everything you have said about your grandmother is about how much she loved to cook and sew and work in her gardens. She would not have been happy being confined to her bed and unable to move."

'I think what you dreamt was the truth, Sarah. That's what she would have wanted for you. She obviously loved you a great deal. I'm sure it meant more to your grandmother that you came to see her and the bouquet of flowers wasn't what was important to her,' Beth commented.

Sarah wiped her eyes and tried to absorb what Caroline and Beth were saying.

"I so wanted to feel relief from my pain, my grandmother's death was such a monumental event in my early life that I have little memory of the remaining years in elementary school and middle school.

"High school memories continue to stay with me and bring a smile to my face. I attended a large high school where there were a number of groups. There was one group of 'high-achievers'. They were a group of smart kids who some of us thought of as a little strange. They were special, as their intelligence was somewhat intimidating to the rest of us. A second group was comprised of kids who were quiet and who we thought of as anti-social. That group seemed most content to stay together and not mingle with the rest of the student body. The third group was made up of the outgoing students, the socially popular, heroes of the sports teams, the handsome, sexy cool guys and the cute girls. We were known as the party kids."

"That doesn't surprise me a bit," joked Caroline.

"Although I was part of that popular group, my parents were strict and didn't allow me to go out very much. I was allowed to go out with friends very occasionally so I often arranged a sleepover night at my friend Emma's house on Friday or Saturday evenings just so I could get out of the house to a place where we were free to hang with our friends.

"When I was fourteen and just starting high school, my parents decided my grandfather could no longer live alone and convinced him to sell his house and move in with us. I loved the fact that he was coming to live with us as my world lightened somewhat with him in the house, even though it wasn't the same as when we visited our grandparents. My grandmother wasn't with him and he wasn't the same man. While I think he liked living with us and having the family around, I think he continued to feel a terrible sense of loneliness from the loss of my grandmother. My grandfather added another dimension to the family dynamics though and became the one who was up early on school mornings to cook breakfast before sending us out the door to school. At dinner, he sat at the opposite corner from me at the dinner table, to my mother's right, and although he seldom participated in any table conversation, I always saw him listening intently if my siblings or I was talking. He was the one adult in the house who seemed to have the most interest in what was happening in my world.

"I was sixteen and in my junior year when I got my driver's license and thought, at last, I would have some freedom and even escape the house, but I was wrong. While I had the status of holding a license, it didn't help at all because I was seldom allowed to drive the car. I was not unlike every teenager who prefers to be with friends and in my case away from the house. I looked for reasons to be out of the house sometimes at events I cared little about."

"Did you have a boyfriend, Sarah?"

"Not really, Beth. I was a good student and loved going to school. I enjoyed my classes for the most part but struggled in my chemistry class. I had no trouble memorizing aspects of the course like the Periodic Table, but could not for the life of me figure out what to do with formulas and beakers or their purpose during lab. One day I embarrassed myself in front of my classmates when I spilled a beaker of acid down the front of my dress, causing the teacher to react as though it were a serious emergency. I was accompanied to the nurse's office where I was cleaned up and returned to class. My lab partner, Dan, expressed concern and indicated his willingness to help me so a similar incident wouldn't happen again. I was just very embarrassed by the scene I had created among my peers.

"Dan was a year younger than I but I thought nothing of it. He was handsome and had a warm smile with deep dimples. His smile revealed a small chip in his front tooth which seemed to only enhance his physical appeal. His hair was combed and waxed back in the same style that Elvis Presley wore his; not a hair out of place. Dan had very blue eyes which sparkled when he smiled. Chemistry quickly became my favorite class, particularly on lab days when Dan and I could chat and flirt as we poured liquids from one beaker to the other."

"That's probably why you spilled the beaker of acid down the front of your dress, Sarah," Beth chided.

"After a few weeks, Dan asked me to go out on a date. In those days there weren't many places to go on a date beside the movies or the bowling alley, so we chose a movie on that first night. We had a nice time and I began to feel I needed to take interest in how I looked."

"Although I was a little overweight, I wanted to look the best I could. All the girls were wearing stylish straight skirts that my mother objected to and forbid, as she thought they were too provocative. After months of begging to be like all the other girls, my mother relented and took me shopping. As I tried on different outfits, what my mother finally consented to was a straight skirt, three sizes larger than what I would have normally worn. The result was this new piece of clothing was no different than that which I had previously owned. In fact, it was even a little more hideous as it was obviously a straight skirt 'gathered' at the waist. I looked like I was wearing a potato sack!"

Beth and Caroline laughed at the picture Sarah had conjured up. Once Caroline stopped laughing, she managed to squeak, "Did you actually wear it that way?"

Sarah replied, "Sort of. Wait till I tell you what I did. You won't believe it!"

"You know what peer pressure was like being a teenager. I so desperately wanting to be like the other girls in school but my clothes were hideous. My best friend Emma took pity on me and offered to share her clothes with me. Her outfits were stylish, matching sweaters with wool straight skirts, appropriate jewelry as accessories. Each morning, Emma brought me one of her matching outfits where, as soon as the opening school bell rang, we would meet in the lavatory. I would quickly take my ugly outdated clothes I'd left the house in that morning, stuff them in my book bag and leave the lavatory beautifully attired in her fashionable clothes."

"Oh gosh, Sarah, that is hysterical! How long did you do that? Didn't any of your classmates ever figure out you and Emma had the same outfits on different days?" Caroline asked.

"No. I did that all year and if any of my classmates had noticed anything strange, they never mentioned it."

"I think your plan was ingenuous!" Caroline remarked.

Through giggles, Beth suggested, "Perhaps the rest of the students just thought you two shopped together!"

"At last I felt as though I fit into the class. I didn't stand out in frumpy clothes that were outdated and too big for me. I used Emma's clothes for the entire year; no one in school was the wiser that they weren't my clothes. My mother never found out about the outfits but she did find out about something else I did every school day and there was Hell to pay.

"Girls were wearing makeup, not a whole lot, just a little mascara and a touch of lipstick. I was not permitted to wear any makeup, of course. I knew the use of makeup was an impossible battle to fight. You won't believe this one either! I struggled to no avail with my father each rainy morning when he insisted, I wear red rubber boots like a six-year-old. My embarrassment was beyond anyone's imagination. I knew a makeup battle was out of the realm of possibilities.

"Along with her outfits, Emma shared her makeup which I carefully applied each morning and carefully removed each afternoon after last period - with the exception of one day. I have no memory of what interrupted my practice of going to the lavatory at the end of the day but I clearly remember what happened when I arrived home from school. I was no sooner inside the front door, when my mother turned and screamed in horror. She walked over, slapped me across the face and screamed that she would report my behavior to my father when he got home;

I would be punished, which I was. My punishment didn't stop me though in my attempts to fit in with my classmates. I continued to wear Emma's clothes and makeup. My punishment just taught me to be more careful.

"Dan and I walked the halls together, and of course chemistry took on a whole new meaning. Dan had his own car, a pink Dodge which today would be scoffed at but in the late 1950's was viewed as a sports car. We began dating and I grew to love him for not only his gentleness and sense of humor, but his family. Often after picking me up for a date, instead of going bowling or to a movie, we preferred to go to his house where we might play a card game with his parents or sisters. He was the only boy in the family with three older sisters who treated him as a younger brother in need of 'mothering'.

"Dan's parents were so unlike mine. His mother laughed and gave every indication of enjoying hearing whatever we had to say. His father was more subdued and less vocal but was quick to smile. I felt welcomed in Dan's home and had little interest in necessarily going anywhere else on our date nights. It was as though I had found a family; one that appreciated me and enjoyed my company. It felt almost like being back in my grandparent's home.

"Dan and I went steady through his junior year which was my senior year. Despite our age and class difference, my circle of friends accepted Dan and included him in everything we did. Because each of us had a prom to attend our junior and senior years, I enjoyed the advantage of being able to attend two – his junior and, in the same year, my senior.

"The summer after my graduation passed quickly; faster than I had wanted it to, as I knew the time was fast approaching for me to go to college, and leave Dan behind.

He was entering his senior year and because I was going to be away, we agreed that we should each see other people and date others without feeling as though we were cheating on the other. We rationalized that his senior year and my freshman year at college were each too important to shut ourselves away from having a good time.

"Right after Labor Day, my parents drove me to college where I would spend the next two years. The college was small with six brick dormitories arranged in a circle. After setting up my dorm room and meeting my roommate, my parents said they had a long drive back home and they had better get started to leave. I can still see their car pulling away from the curb as I stood in front of the dorm stairs. I watched their station wagon until it disappeared in the trees. Waving until they were no longer in my sight then, taking a deep breath, I turned and walked up the stairs to my room on the third floor. I was looking forward with mixed emotions to my new beginning; filled with the excitement of being on my own and, conversely, the fear of the responsibility of being on my own. Deciding to make the most of this new beginning, I threw myself totally into dorm activities.

"I liked my roommate, although she was a serious student and not quick to laugh or even to enjoy dorm life. She actually transferred to a different school after the first year. Our dormitory had a room in the basement we called 'the butt" because that was where smoking was permitted, card games played and where we all gathered on Thursday nights in front of the television to watch Dr. Kildare. I made friends easily but wanted to do well in school, so I focused more on studies than boys."

"Loved Dr. Kildare!", both women exclaimed

"Dan and I wrote to each other almost every day and talked by phone when he was allowed to call once a week. In late October, Dan surprised me one Saturday by coming to visit. It was so good to see him and he seemed as happy to see me. We had a wonderful weekend. The New England foliage was at its peak and we were able to take long walks in the woods reconnecting and sharing stories of how we had spent our first month without the other. Dan was excited about the football season and looking forward in another month to the start of his favorite sport, ice hockey.

"Sunday afternoon came and all too suddenly it was time for him to leave. Just like you, Beth, I have a hard time saying goodbye. Goodbyes always create for me the same kind of feeling you talked about; a sadness and emptiness. When Dan was about to leave that sense of abandonment rushed in and all I could say was 'I'll see you soon' to avoid any sense of finality with his departure. We reassured each other of how much love we felt for one another. I wished him a safe trip, told him I'd see him in a month when I was home for Thanksgiving and, for a second time, stood in front of the steps of the dorm waving someone off as they disappeared down the driveway.

"As a small woman's college isolated in a remote part of New England, the college administration arranged functions for the students to meet students at a nearby men's college. These functions were called 'mixers' so we all would mix! I decided not to go to the first two mixers but by the beginning of November, I was tired of sitting alone in the dorm on a Saturday afternoon and decided I would go and try one. The bus left on Saturday morning in time to watch a rugby or football game in the afternoon prior to an informal supper in the college dining room.

A dance followed dinner until midnight when we would board the bus and return to our campus.

"I have no recollection of the circumstances of how I met Jake, a second-year student enrolled in the pre-med program, as well as, a star football player on the college team. We seemed to fall easily into conversation and before the night was over, we made plans to see each other the following weekend and the weekend after that. As I was boarding the bus to leave after the second weekend, Jake invited me to attend his college holiday dance on the first Saturday night of December. I accepted but, as soon as I had, experienced a twinge of guilt. Despite the fact Dan and I had agreed it was in each of our best interests to see others, I knew Dan had not been seeing anyone, and I felt guilt.

"When I spoke to Dan, I told him on the phone I had accepted a date to go to a dance in a few weeks with someone I had just met. Dan was quiet and I knew I had hurt him, which caused more guilt on my part but I knew Thanksgiving break was coming in a few weeks and knew I would talk to Dan face to face and smooth things over and assure him that my relationship with Jake was not serious. In no way would Jake interfere with Dan's and my relationship. Nonetheless, I could tell that I had hurt him and I felt badly."

"I arrived home for Thanksgiving break on the day before the holiday and enjoyed a family celebration with many cousins, aunts and uncles on Thursday. My mother was excited to learn I had met a young man at what she thought of as a prestigious college and even more excited when I told her I needed to go shopping for a formal dress, as I had been invited to the holiday dance the following weekend.

"My mother and I set out early Friday morning the day after Thanksgiving. Remembering how horrendous it was to shop for clothes with her when I was in high school, I dreaded the day figuring it was going to be a struggle for each of us to get through the day without wanting to kill each other. While I was excited to be trying on elegant dresses, I was more excited about the date I had that evening with Dan. I could think of little else. I was excited to see him and anxious to put his mind at ease and erase my sense of guilt. There was that guilt again! I hadn't been given a second chance to bring flowers to my grandmother, but I knew I could make everything right with Dan that night."

"I'm getting worried about what you're going to say, Sarah." Caroline said.

"Dan and I had talked on Wednesday as soon as I had arrived home and knew that with the holiday and family, we would have to wait until Friday night to see each other. We had talked and decided we wanted just a quiet spot for our date. I said I wanted to stop by his house to say hello to his parents and then we could go grab a burger at the local hangout. I was counting hours until I saw him and could convince him to his face how deeply I still cared for him.

"Miraculously and painlessly, in a few hours, my mother and I found a pink brocade dress we both thought appropriate for the occasion. We even found an ideal pair of shoes for the dress. The dress was expensive, but my mother graciously didn't object. I think she was as pleased as I that we had effortlessly found a dress which fit perfectly and was so beautiful. I think she was happy for me and wanted me to look my best at the dance."

"I'm glad it was a nice memory for you, Sarah. I half expected you to say your mother insisted on something hideous after the straight-skirt story you told us about," Beth commented.

"We shopped for an inexpensive necklace and earrings to accessorize my dress so by the time we finally arrived home from shopping it was the middle of the afternoon. I had plenty of time to wash my hair, put it in rollers and shower. Dan was picking me up at six o'clock."

"It was about five-thirty and I was in my bedroom choosing what I would wear when the phone rang. I heard my mother say, 'Just a moment please.' I met my mother halfway down the stairs as she handed me the phone. I barely had time to say, 'Hello' when one of Dan's friends frantically asked, 'Sarah, did you hear about Dan? He collapsed at ice hockey practice this afternoon. He was taken by ambulance to the hospital. Here's the number.'

"I ran back upstairs to the privacy of my room. Shaking, I dialed the hospital number and after giving my name, said, "I'm calling to find out about Daniel Ingram'. There was a pause before the operator sadly replied, 'I'm sorry. Daniel Ingram was dead on arrival'."

"Oh Sarah, when you started talking about your high school days and how you changed your outfits every day, I thought you were going to tell us another funny story. My heart hurts for you. I can't imagine how you must have felt. The shock! The pain! You were so young. No one should have had to go through that at seventeen," Beth whispered.

"I can imagine how devastated you were. Were you thinking of your grandmother when you said that twice you felt such tremendous guilt and hadn't had a second chance to change it?" Caroline asked. Sarah responded with a nod.

Caroline handed Sarah a tissue and gave her a hug.

"I just had a terrible feeling that something horrendous was about to happen when you were telling us that story, Sarah," Caroline said. If you want to talk, please call."

Beth remained deep in thought as Sarah's feelings of guilt and remorse had reminded Beth of her own. It was late; everyone was emotionally exhausted. There was no rush thought Beth. My story can wait.

A few weeks later Sarah asked Beth about her train trip to Illinois which opened the door for Beth.

Beth

January 1960

"At the end of the second day of travel to Illinois, my parents and I were met at the train station by Ellen and John. They were my parent's age, in their mid-forties and had married late in life ten years earlier. Ellen was an elementary school teacher while John was a writer at the corporate level of a manufacturing company, an editor of the company's literature. I said hello when I greeted them at the station, but felt shy. I didn't know what to say. I didn't know them, had no idea what it was going to be like living with them, felt abandoned by my parents and filled with shame. Should I say something like, 'It's nice to meet you. Thanks for taking me in.'? I listened to the adult chatter on the ride to their home while I sat silently in the backseat. I gathered from what they were saying, they had either married too late in life to have children, were unable to or chose not to. In any case, for whatever reason they didn't have children.

"We pulled up to a fairly new building in a suburban neighborhood. John and Ellen lived on the second floor of the two-story walk-up building in a two- bedroom apartment big enough for them but a bit crowded for three. We unloaded the car and we were given a tour of the apartment. The kitchen and living room were quite spacious, while the master bedroom was large enough to accommodate two twin beds. The smallest room, a den and TV room, was to be my room and I would sleep on the pull-out couch.

"I didn't see much of my father and mother the next day as they were off to a bunch of meetings which I didn't hear about until two days later when the five of us sat in the living room. My father informed me that a man named Mr. Lenox would be coming to the apartment three days a week and would tutor me in four subjects. My father had somehow arranged with the local high school that I would enroll in their school but as a homebound student. Upon completion, my high school records would be forwarded to my school back home ensuring that every detail would appear to be authentic and support the story I had told to all my friends as to why I was living away from home."

"I'm sure that, as an educator, you must see it was pretty ingenious of your father. No one would be the wiser that you didn't actually attend classes." Caroline pointed out.

"Two days after that first meeting, a second meeting was held in the living room. I sat silently as my father told me he had made arrangements with an organization called Catholic Family Services for the purpose of managing the legal aspects of the baby's adoption. He told me I would take a bus to the building where this organization was located and meet regularly with a nun to discuss procedures, questions and my concerns. My father spoke to me very matter-of-factly as though I were creating a grocery list. I was sixteen and didn't even know how to communicate to anyone what my concerns were. Was I supposed to talk about my fears, the loneliness I was already feeling, being separated from my friends, my shame, and my embarrassment, not to mention my guilt? How was I supposed to discuss any of this with a stranger when I was emotionally unavailable to anyone except my closest friend, Jane? I had withdrawn from everyone and everything around me behind my self-imposed armor.

"The next day, John, Ellen and I drove my parents to the train station. My parents gave me a hug, a pat on the back from my father and peck on the cheek from my mom. I waved goodbye as I stood and watched them board their train. I thought my mother was crying, but I wasn't sure. I wanted to believe I was wrong as I didn't want to add more guilt to what I was already feeling.

"After leaving my parents at the train station, we dropped John at work and Ellen took me to the office of my new doctor. He was a friend of John and Ellen's and was well aware of my entire situation. He was a kind man and, over the months, I felt he went out of his way to show me compassion and unspoken understanding. Although kind, he was adamant about my health. After an examination, he met with Ellen and me and handed us a list of guidelines for my care. I was told what I would be allowed to eat for breakfast and lunch; for supper I would be permitted one hamburger patty and a bowl of green beans every night during the remaining six months of my pregnancy. This diet would mean that I wouldn't gain more than eighteen pounds. My baby was due in June which fit in beautifully with 'our story'; a separation from my mother for the remainder of the school year. The web of deceit we were creating was in place. I would be back home at the end of the 'make believe' school year in June, the problems between my mother and me resolved and life would continue with no one the wiser."

"My gosh. It's easy to see why you have abandonment issues, Beth" Sarah remarked. "Come on…first Jack leaves you and within two months your parents have left you. You're right. It doesn't take a rocket scientist to figure out the why."

"You know, I find it strange that I look back now and can picture where the chairs were in each room, the various shades of gold and green of the floral prints on the upholstered chairs in John and Ellen's living room, the card table in the middle of the room where Mr. Lenox and I sat three afternoons a week. I recall the emptiness of each day. Waking up in the morning and knowing that John and Ellen were leaving for work, I wondered what I would do with myself that day. There was nowhere to go; I studied but essentially had nothing to do. I had no friends, no social interaction with anyone my age, and for eight hours each day would wait until John and Ellen returned home from work.

"In the early 1970's, there were no cell phones and further I had been given strict orders that I wasn't to communicate with anyone. I could only communicate through letters which I was permitted to write with the stipulation established by my father, that each letter to friends was to be written, copied for future reference, and read for approval by John before mailed. The purpose of my letters was to paint a picture to everyone that I was happy in my new home and had, in a short period of time, made numerous friends. My letters were filled with exaggerated accounts of adventures common to a typical sixteen-year-old. My letters continued to cultivate the farce I was living."

"What did you do all day, Beth? Did you just sit around and watch television?" Sarah asked.

"Pretty much, but I studied too. One day, out of desperation, I asked Ellen to take me to the yarn shop and asked if I could have some money to buy needles and yarn to knit a scarf. I started to knit and couldn't stop. I knit to keep my hands busy. I didn't even think about what I was knitting, but just kept knitting as pieces of yarn grew to thin long pieces of knitted wool that I called a scarf. It could have been a blanket. When the first 'scarf' was finished, I started another. I kept knitting. I knit endlessly for six months.

"Since I grew up in a quiet neighborhood surrounded by woods, I wasn't used to city life that began about two blocks away from John and Ellen's apartment. The first few times I took the city bus alone to get to my doctor appointment and Catholic Family Services, I was nervous. But by the end of the first month, I started to look forward to having somewhere to go; a reason to get out of bed in the morning.

"My doctor visits once a month were short; a quick examination and weigh- in but my appointments with Catholic Family Services were more involved. Each time I was taken into a stark office to sit at a desk across from a stern, unsmiling woman – a nun who I assumed was assigned to me to offer some sort of counseling. I gave little information in response to an endless stream of questions. She always asked me if I had any questions. Was there anything I wanted to talk to her about? Did I know what to expect? When! Where! How! I just recall squirming in my seat as she threw question after question at me while all I wanted was to get out of that room and for this part of my life to be over. Of course, I couldn't admit that to anyone - certainly not a nun representing the Church and God. She asked me questions about my knowing what was right; what was wrong; what was ethical, and what was not. She urged me to continue attending church to pray for my soul and convinced me it was essential that I go to confession and confess the sins I had committed.

"The following Saturday afternoon, John, Ellen and I went to confession at the Catholic Church we attended every Sunday and on religious holidays. After initiating my confession with the words used to begin all confessions, 'Forgive me Father for I have sinned', I confessed my sins to the priest who was concealed from my view by a small draped scrap of fabric. I was crying. With his chin resting on his hand, he whispered, 'You have committed a mortal sin and will burn in Hell. Go say your penance and ask for forgiveness.' I left the confessional booth, my legs barely able to carry me to the pew to say my penance; experiencing yet another abandonment, now by the Church-seemingly by God."

"How dare he?" Caroline remarked passionately. "How could anyone, priest or not, be so insensitive to a child? It's not as though you weren't scared enough!"

"The days passed slowly with little excitement. I remember one day passing a bakery while walking to the bus stop and felt an uncontrollable desire to treat myself to a chocolate chip cookie. I had no money of my own but was given a meager allowance to buy something I might need such as more yarn. I recall clearly this one day, walking into the bakery and standing before the large glass case, my mouth watering with the aroma. I was hesitant; which cookie to choose - clearly the largest. I took a chance and bought it. It was the most delicious thing I had tasted in months. I hated to swallow each mouthful and lose the flavor. By then, I was barely able to swallow another hamburger patty or pile of green beans. I savored each morsel of that cookie, feeling immediate guilt for having sinfully broken the rules dictated to me by my doctor. 'Please,' I prayed to God, 'don't let the scales tattle on me.'"

"Did they?" Caroline wondered, smiling.

"The scales kept my secret but, let me tell you something! To this day, I cannot swallow a bite of hamburger or a green bean."

"I was lonely. Each day ran into the next. Sometimes I wandered through the house or walked aimlessly through the neighborhood; a walk to the mailbox was an adventure. I dreaded each visit to Catholic Family Services. What would I hear next? When would they give up trying to reform me, trying to show me the depth of my sins, trying to teach me right from wrong, trying to convince me that turning to God was my only salvation? The priests and nuns told me that I should pray for the strength to give over to Him. I agreed but the Him seemed cold and distant, not kind. I wanted to hear from, the 'him' that would take away my loneliness, but he had run away."

"John and Ellen did all they could to be kind to me and I never felt as though I had intruded on their lives. They always made me feel welcome even though I wasn't in the right frame of mind to be welcomed. I just didn't trust anyone except myself. I felt I was the one I could depend on. Since everyone had pretty much left me, I would show them I didn't need anyone else. I wouldn't let myself down as they had. If my security and happiness were dependent on only me, then I couldn't be abandoned again."

"Do you still feel that way Beth? I can see how you might but I want you to know you're not alone if Sarah and I are here for you. We won't let you down."

"I know that which is why I can share all of this with you. Ellen arrived home around four-thirty, John an hour later. I was like a puppy who had been left alone during the day and clamored for the company of anyone after a long day of solitude. If I had a tail to wag when Ellen walked in the door, it would have been wagging back and forth frantically with glee. John cooked dinner while Ellen and I gathered each night at the kitchen table to keep him company; Ellen enjoying a cocktail while I sat at the same table just happy to hear voices. John never cooked dinner without first putting on one of his favorite records. He loved a blues singer named Leadbelly, and would stand in front of the stove clapping his hands and stomping his foot while my burger cooked. That was my merriment! I can still see him standing by the stove with his apron, while we laughed as he was flipping my burger to the beat of the music."

"I would have gagged if I had to eat a burger every day for six months" exclaimed Caroline as she pointed a finger down her throat to drive home her point.

"After dinner, we all sat in my room and watched something on television. I knit while they watched a baseball game or some other program in which I had little interest. But then I had little interest in much of anything – certainly not in life."

Sarah hesitated then asked, "Did you feel differently when you first felt the baby move?"

"I don't think it ever registered with me. I was so numb and detached from life and so sadly from the baby.

"I learned in March that Jack had been found and returned home. I heard this from Jane who had figured out a way to communicate with me through the mail without anyone knowing. She would write and tell me everything that was happening at home and in school, then carefully mail her letter over the weekend so that it would be delivered to me during the weekday when I was alone and could get the mail from the box. I always wrote a letter back right away then walked down the street to the post office box at the corner to deposit my letter. It was a relief to be able to write to Jane about what was really happening, not the fake made-up things. This was the only contact I had with friends and Jane was the only person I allowed to know how I really felt; she was the only one I trusted to get inside my shield. She was my pipeline and I lived through her to know about what was happening with Jack and the friends I'd left behind."

"You must have been so relieved to know Jack was alright, weren't you?" Caroline asked.

"Absolutely, but I don't know what I expected! I was glad he was safe but he sure as Hell wasn't going to come rescue me. My heart ached for him though. Once he had returned home, he began to send messages to me through Jane. One day I went to the mailbox to discover a package from Jane but it was actually from Jack. Inside the box was a set of rosary beads and white prayer book with a note tucked inside. The note read 'Dear Beth. I'm so sorry for everything that happened. I am so worried about you. I care about you so much and wish I could do something to help you. I feel so helpless. Is there anything you need?' He signed the note, 'All my love, Jack'.

"Was there anything I needed? I needed him! How I needed him! Jack wasn't Catholic but somehow, I read his religious gifts to be his way of providing me with the strength that he thought he couldn't – that of the church.

With Jack's choice of gifts, I wondered if there was a double meaning. Was he sending me a message that I was safe in God's care, urging me to trust God since he himself wasn't physically or emotionally able to help me? I cried a lot that day.

"I was determined that no one was going to know the pain I was feeling – no one would see outside what I was feeling inside. I put on a stoic front and went through the motions of living. The last person I wanted to know how I was feeling was Jack. After all, I thought he loved me. I had made a very impulsive foolish mistake for which I was paying the price. I had trusted him. He hadn't been sent away. He hadn't been abandoned by his family. He was back in school enjoying all aspects of a normal high school experience. He was a coward. He had abandoned me; run away and let me face the situation alone. I wrote what I would call short, pointed perfunctory letters; always polite, never revealing that life wasn't idyllic and I wasn't fine. To everyone, I was always fine. I thought I could have counted on him but he had let me down and there was no way I would ask for anything from him."

It was clear that both women felt Beth's pain. They noticed as Beth spoke, her jaw had clenched in anger.

As Beth spoke, there was occasionally a tone of bitterness to her voice, particularly when she repeated her determination to not let anyone see the pain she was experienced. There was a resolve in her voice.

"I cannot believe you didn't hate Jack at that point", Sarah remarked.

Caroline quickly added, "I hope you never felt guilty about your anger. Let's face it. Your anger was more than justified."

"Oh, there were times when I was so angry, I think I did hate him. In the spring, just when I thought I couldn't withstand any more pain, Jane wrote to me about their junior prom. I couldn't face the thought of another betrayal so I convinced myself that she probably thought she was doing me a favor to keep me in the loop of everything was happening at school. What hurt most was that she wrote she was going to the prom with Jack. I didn't expect him to sit home but the news crushed me. I thought how can he possibly go to the prom as though nothing had changed? How dare he not have to give up something, to do without as I had to do. He had left me alone in a cowardly act, returning to his life as though nothing had happened while I was unable to go on with mine carrying a life within me that we were both responsible for creating."

"You must have felt betrayed. Anyone would. Do you think Jane thought if she went with him, nothing would come of it because they were just friends? Maybe she was trying to protect you." Sarah suggested.

"What do you mean, Sarah?"

"Maybe Jane thought if Jack went to the prom with another girl, it might lead to something else and it would be harder on you. "

"I don't know what her reasoning was, Sarah, but I'll admit initially that it stung.

"The imaginary plan continued to go as scheduled through the spring and into early June. I had grown quite large and uncomfortable but with the warmer weather and winter in the past, I could see the light at the end of the tunnel. It was almost over. Within a month I would be back with my friends. I missed my friends but not my home. The school year would end in another three weeks and I would sadly, with tears in my eyes, have to leave my imaginary friends, Susie and Tim, and return to New England, resume the life I had left six months ago and all would be well. But the best laid plans of mice and men…'"

"Why, what happened, Beth?" Caroline asked.

"While I was technically due to deliver the baby at the beginning of June, I missed my due date and two weeks later the doctor decided to induce labor. This new development threw a crimp into the timing of THE PLAN. Everyone scrambled to create a new plan to coincide with the revised timing. The later date of the birth would raise questions about why I wasn't coming home at the end of the school year. To solve the problem, my father created an imaginary vacation with Susie, my new friend, and an invitation by her family to join them for two weeks at their summer home on the lake.

"Once more I wrote a letter with a carbon copy so I could study it and remember what I had said and the story I created. I mailed it to my parents begging for permission to PLEASE let me stay a few weeks longer. Of course, they gave me permission and hoped I would have a wonderful vacation at the lake. The date for inducing my baby allowed for a week or two of recovery; induce the baby, add some time for recovery, then head home. On the chosen day, I was brought to the hospital early in the morning."

Caroline interrupted. "Were you terrified, Beth?"

"I don't think I felt anything. I saw the day as the beginning of the end. The first day of getting my life back and starting again. My delivery was scheduled for first thing in the morning. I don't remember anything before I was given an injection and within a half hour began to feel the pain radiating from my back to my stomach – severe cramps. Someone came in and gave me another injection. I recall being observed and examined for the next few hours, but

I was out of it, almost sub-conscious but very aware of the severe pains. I was in and out of consciousness and was aware that after about five hours, I was wheeled into an operating room. I remember looking up at the blinding ceiling lights, squirming restlessly, trying to move away from the pain. The last words I heard from a nurse, as I fell into oblivion were, 'She looks so young'.

"When I woke up, I was still in the operating room. I sensed something was wrong. There was a lot of movement in the room; many people seemed to be scurrying about. I was given more sedation and faded back into oblivion again.

"The next time I woke up, I was lying in a hospital bed in a different room. I didn't feel any pain either physically or emotionally. I was numb to everything. I was resting in a slightly elevated position when I opened my eyes to see John and Ellen standing beside me. I turned my head and saw a variety of bags filled with colored liquids hanging from shiny silver poles. Ellen said, 'Don't look. Don't worry. You just rest. Everything will be fine.'

"I was aware of wires and tubes coming in and out from all parts of me. I asked them to tell me what had happened. I could tell they were hesitant to answer but said that there was a problem with the placenta and uterus but everything was going to be fine. Ellen said the baby had weighed ten pounds and I was torn and bleeding but the doctors had taken care of it. I would be fine. Ellen gave me a kiss on the cheek and assured me I had the best doctor and the best care. I would be fine. I wasn't told the extent of the hemorrhaging or given any further hint that I was in trouble."

"My gosh, how scared you must have been. Did you think you were dying, Beth?" Caroline asked. "I understand

John and Ellen told you what the problem was but they didn't say what it all meant."

"I was so heavily sedated; I was totally out of it. I was barely conscious; not even enough to ask about the baby. I'm ashamed to admit that."

"Ellen and John left with the promise that they would be in touch with the doctor during the night and would monitor my situation by phone from home. They each gave me another kiss on the cheek and assured me they would be back first thing in the morning. I slept. I faded in and out of deep sleep but, at some point during the night, I awakened with the sensation that there was someone standing beside the bed. I forced myself to open my eyes and was surprised to see a man, dressed in a black suit with a white collar leaning over me. I squinted and realized that it was a priest. He held a cross in his hand as he swept it back and forth over me. Despite my semi-conscious state of mind, I heard him praying; asking God to help me. He asked for God's forgiveness on my behalf. He touched my hand and whispered, 'You are forgiven my child. Bless you in the name of the Father, the Son and Holy Ghost.' His words and touch seemed to squeeze my chest and heart. In my semi-conscious state, I was unable to cry and relieve the pent-up pressure."

"Do you think there was really a priest or did you dream it, Beth?" Sarah asked.

"I did question in the morning if I had just dreamt it but decided that was something John and Ellen would have arranged with the church. I slept fitfully throughout the night waiting for morning. I watched a large clock on the wall over the door at the foot of the bed through the night, as it moved slowly toward morning. I didn't know what tomorrow would hold. The clock became a diversion and kept my eyes off the tubes, wires and plastic bags."

Sarah thoughtfully observed. "For months we have been sharing the trauma we each experienced during our teenage years. Doesn't it just make you wonder how many other women out there have had the same struggles? Look at us though! All three of us lived through horrendous experiences in our childhoods which could have destroyed us. But we're here. We made it and we're successful!" Sarah enthusiastically remarked.

"Absolutely! You're so right!" agreed Caroline.

"I'm so happy you still enjoy knitting, Beth, or we might not all be here tonight" Sarah added.

Beth replied, "Wait till I tell you what I did. But I'm exhausted. Let's save it for another time."

"I can't say my life with Steve has been all bad because when it's good, it's very good. But when it was bad, oh, it's very bad. But you're right, Sarah. We're all here. We've survived." Caroline said.

Sarah was anxious to share. "Before we leave for the night, I want you both to know how excited I am that the seller of the house with the pond accepted our offer last night! We'll put our house on the market and hopefully it will sell quickly. I can't wait for you both to see the house. It was built in the 1700s and is going to be the perfect setting for my antique collections. I love it!"

The three women gave each other a hug, as they did every Wednesday when they parted, and wished each other a good night.

Over the course of the next few weeks, Caroline talked about her marriage to Steve and felt safe to share what had been happening most recently.

"Steve and I began to spend every weekend together on his sailboat. I was traveling a great deal throughout the States and Canada during the week but every Friday after work we drove to the boat for the weekend and returned home Sunday night. This new life felt like an adventure as I'd been married to Bill right after school and had never experienced the fun of dating and adventure. It was as though I had been transported to a different planet as a young teenager."

"We anchored in small harbors along the coast and took the dinghy to shore in the late afternoons to enjoy dinner at outdoor summer restaurants. Occasionally we would take longer trips – two or three days sailing before reaching a destination, usually another small harbor. Sleeping in the V berth and looking up at the stars at night through the hatch was magical. I grew used to the gentle rocking of the boat, counting on it to lull me to sleep.

"I learned quickly how to make my way around the cramped galley and use the 'head'. Showers were on deck with a large plastic bag filled with water warmed by the sun or just a dive overboard. Steve was a very good sailor and I seldom felt afraid although once or twice I did feel somewhat vulnerable. When I stopped to think that if something happened to Steve out on the water, I would have no idea how to get back to shore, sail the boat or even turn on the engine. Steve was a certified sailing instructor which helped to calm my fears; he was confident on his boat and I usually felt relaxed. Each experience with Steve was so new to me that it felt as though I was living in a different world compared to my previous mundane life. We sailed through storms before anchoring in harbors with lightning and claps of thunder. I listened as he told me about sailing through a bad storm, a few years ago, when lightning struck the mainsail and burned out the engine and navigation system.

"As I got to know Steve better, he shared that his father who had died about twenty years ago, had always enjoyed the sea and had taken over the marina from his father."

"So, the marina that Steve owns has been in his family for generations?" Beth asked.

"Right. He told me how his father had owned a trawler, and while his father preferred motoring over sailing, Steve was accustomed to spending time on the water. He spoke with sadness of his mother who had died of cancer when Steve was only thirteen. He talked about the night she was taken by ambulance from the house as he watched from his upstairs bedroom window, his next memory was seeing his mother lying on a table in the living room of their home as people cried and prayed around her."

"That's a bit strange, don't you think?" one of the women asked.

"The only thing I can think of was she was lying in the living room for calling hours but I agree, it is very strange," Caroline thought.

"He related how devastated his father had been. Although his father continued to work, he was a different man, detached from his family and inconsolable. Without a mother, Steve and his siblings were sent away to private schools; Steve to a school in Europe where he lived for a few years. He had little memory of his years there, at least that's what he said. One time though, Steve alluded to a nagging sense that something terrible had happened to him at the school but was unable to recall the incident. Or at least, if he remembered, he never shared it with me.

"A few years after his mother's death, Steve was brought back to the States to live with his father and his new step-mother. He was vague about other family information which I attributed as either too painful to reveal or something he would continue to share as we got to know each other better. Oftentimes when he spoke of his family, I watched his eyes and noted that they would suddenly dart to the side for no apparent reason. I could tell he didn't realize his eyes moved but, in later years, he would marvel at my ability to know he was thinking about something he wished to forget. When it happened, I would notice and ask, 'What were you just thinking?' He would smile and ask, 'How do you know?' without ever answering my question. I was too much in love to see what the movement of his eyes meant or to imagine the gesture might be related to any other issues.

"Steve had two children, a son who was married and living in the Midwest and a daughter who was as much a sailor at heart as her father. She worked in the marine business and at eighteen was content to live the haphazard life of a teenager with no worries. She lived as a free spirit with her mother near Steve's business so we saw her often. Steve was very close to his daughter as they not only had similar personalities but they shared a love of sailing and being on the water."

"When Steve and I weren't sailing or working, we Had a great time playing. We went out to dinners often, went to movies, attended the theater or went dancing. I felt like a teenager being pampered by a man who genuinely enjoyed being with me. Steve's business essentially took care of itself, leaving him with a great deal of spare time and no need to necessarily live near it. I owned a small house about forty-five minutes away and it wasn't long before Steve started to spend the night. By the end of six months, Steve had moved into my home and relinquished his apartment.

"We really enjoyed being together; I felt as though I had found a partner and soulmate. Years later, I would come to the realization that what I provided to Steve was a sense of security and a home. We attended church on Sunday mornings during the winter which I loved. Standing beside Steve in church was very peaceful and bonding for me. It felt right and I looked forward to the experience of the service, which we followed with breakfast at a favorite diner.

"A year after meeting Steve, we were married, and after a send-off by our children, we honeymooned for a week at a nearby inn in a small town filled with small shops. We had developed an interest in antiques and spent the better part of the weekdays hunting for early 19thC pieces we would use to decorate our little house. Life was good and I couldn't believe how lucky I was.

"Returning home, life picked up where we had left off except that rather quickly, I began to see a pattern of behavior with Steve that I'd not seen before. While I was at work, if he wasn't checking in at his business, he would spend time in the basement crafting pieces or making gifts for me such as a new jewelry box. Once or twice, I noticed that when I returned home from work, it seemed that he had been drinking which surprised me because, before we were married, we might have a glass of wine at dinner, but that was it. There was only one time when we were out and Steve had too much to drink but I passed this off as a rarity and nothing to be concerned with.

"I couldn't believe how happy I was to have a husband that outwardly demonstrated affection toward me. I felt like a princess. Steve would pinch my cheek and say, 'You're so cute.' Or on the spur of the moment, take my hand

and say, 'Let's go buy you a new dress.' I felt loved. This was what I interpreted 'being loved' looked like. I didn't question how he acted and just thought this is what it feels like to be loved. I felt loved when he told me I was cute and sweet, not just because I was smart or accomplished. Everything we did, we did together. We cooked together. We washed dishes together. I washed while Steve dried. We always had music playing in the background while we cleaned up the kitchen and, almost nightly, Steve would remove my soapy hand from the dishpan and say, 'Let's dance' which we did lovingly around the kitchen. I loved this time together so much that when we remodeled the kitchen, I turned down his offer to install a dishwasher to make my life easier. I preferred to wash dishes by hand with the help of my loving husband."

"Caroline, it sounds romantic. I think what you're describing is the kind of behavior that gives you a warm fuzzy feeling," Beth commented. "That's what I was trying to describe when I said I never had that but was what I always wanted. I'm not suggesting I looked for any kind of romantic feelings from my father but just some warmth would have gone a long way. It sounds to me like Steve not only made you feel loved, but loved being with you."

"One afternoon Steve called me at work and suggested we meet at a cocktail lounge after I finished work. I agreed and thought it sounded like fun; maybe it would lead to dinner out as well. I arrived at the lounge to find Steve sitting at the bar with a drink in his hand and it was obvious from his speech, he must have been there for quite a while. I ordered a drink and he ordered another. For the next few hours, he laughed and joked with others at the bar; he was very affectionate and clinging to me to the extent that I was finding it offensive and embarrassing.

"I was starting to feel hungry and decided we needed to go home as it seemed a dinner out was not in Steve's plan. I was also tired after a full day of work and I knew Steve had had too much to drink. I wanted to get him home as I was feeling embarrassed by his loud voice and aggressive behavior. When Steve asked for the check, I excused myself and went to the ladies' room. As I passed through the entrance to the lounge, a man stepped in front of me, put his hand on my arm and said, 'Be careful. I wouldn't go anywhere with that man. He's drunk.' I was shocked and felt my face redden, but immediately became defensive stating foolishly and emphatically, 'That man is my husband. Thank you.'"

"Did the man say anything else to you?" Sarah asked.

"No, he just walked away and I walked into the ladies' room. Steve was in no condition to drive home so we left his car in the lot and planned to pick it up in the morning. I drove the twenty minutes home while Steve sat silently in the passenger seat. When I pulled in the driveway and after turning off the car, I gently asked if he needed help getting out of the car. He turned toward me, snarling with fire in his eyes, 'I don't need your help for anything.' I was stunned at his reaction. I was seeing a side of Steve that was totally new to me. His anger scared me. I felt a prickle run up my spine. Upon entering the house, I didn't dare speak, as Steve staggered to bed. When I left for work the next morning, Steve was still sleeping. I didn't dare even give him a kiss goodbye."

"What do you think happened to him, Caroline? What made him so angry? Do you think it was just because he had had too much to drink?" Sarah asked.

"I don't know," Caroline said "but wait, there's more.

"A week later I saw another side of Steve which scared me further. I was called to a meeting at work late in the day. I called Steve to say I would be a little late and would call when I left the office to give him an hour's notice before I reached home. I was surprised when I arrived home around nine o'clock to find that Steve's car was gone and he was not there. I couldn't think of anywhere he might have gone. The house was dark and Steve had not left a note. I thought perhaps a quick trip to the mall or the grocery store, but again for the house to be dark was unusual.

"I waited, thinking he would be home for a late supper, but after an hour. I made myself a quick sandwich, since Steve clearly wasn't coming home for supper. It did occur to me perhaps he was out at a bar again, but then decided the incident a few weeks ago had been an isolated incident. I waited another hour, very worried, but too embarrassed to call anyone and share my concerns. I walked into our bedroom and adjoining bathroom and noticed immediately his shaving kit and toothbrush, usually on the vanity, were gone! My first reaction was confusion. Then I became somewhat frantic. I had no idea what to think. I had no idea of what the missing shaving kit meant or where he could have gone."

"Did you think he had moved out?"

"I didn't know what to think, Beth. I wondered if I had done something wrong. Had he left because of something I had said? Had something happened to one of his children that pulled him away from home? I had no explanation. I didn't know quite what to do. I didn't know if I should go to bed, sit and wait for his return, or maybe call the police to report my husband missing. When the telephone rang around eleven o'clock, I answered, not knowing if it was going to be the police, a friend or Steve's family on the line.

I was surprised and relieved to hear Steve's voice. His only words were that he was safe and would be home in a day or so, offering no explanation. I was angry that he assumed I was to simply accept his reasons for his disappearance. I decided to keep quiet and not make the situation worse. Steve offered no other information as to where he was or why he had left. I climbed into bed and pulled the covers up to my chin to get warm. I was shaking."

"Why didn't you ask where he went? I would have insisted on an explanation."

"Beth, I had this feeling that I didn't dare rock the boat. I didn't want to push. I guess I was afraid of what I was seeing, or maybe beginning to feel a little afraid of him. An alarm went off in my head as to who was this man I had married. I thought back to my attraction to Steve when I first met him and questioned if my attraction was to him or his adventuresome lifestyle. I didn't want to think that it was simply his ability to be affectionate that had won me over and I'd not looked deeper than how wonderful it felt to feel loved."

"How long was he gone?"

"He came back the next day, Caroline, as promised. He was home when I got back from work and offered little explanation beyond sharing that he remembered his father had a pattern of doing the same thing. When something upset his father, his father would escape to his boat alone for a few days. Steve admitted that he had panicked when I called and told him I would be late. He had immediately felt fearful of being abandoned and had an unexplained urge to leave. I asked what else I could have done beside call and let him know I would be late. He said what he did wasn't my fault and I shouldn't give it another thought. I was uncomfortable with his explanation but wasn't about to press him further. I knew I would keep the incident to myself just as I had with the incident at the bar. I sloughed it off thinking that he had perhaps felt abandoned by me when I didn't return home, bringing up similar feelings of abandonment when his mother died and he had been sent away. Maybe he felt it was easier for him to leave rather than to be left alone.

"For the next few months, we lived in marital bliss but I admit I was guarded, unsure if I would return home and find him gone again. There was no further disappearance, however, and I started to relax. Steve's business continued to flourish requiring little of his time or effort. All was well at my work."

"I don't know what I would have done if I came home and my husband were gone. I don't know what I would have thought. Weren't you angry, Caroline?" asked Sarah.

"I would have been livid that my husband had put me through that fear," added Sarah. "Obviously the difference for me was that Dan had not caused my pain, whereas Steve had a choice. He was selfish, but I understand you said he had problems. I know that doesn't excuse his behavior, but it does help to perhaps understand it."

Sarah had been sitting quietly, absorbed in the conversation, but deep in thought.

"I've been thinking of your concern over finding Steve gone and it's stirring up my feelings of shock after my phone call to the hospital I told you about a few weeks ago. I can feel how painful it was for you, Caroline, when you found Steve gone. I was so stunned after I hung up; it was almost surreal. I immediately questioned if I was having a bad dream. It's late now but next week I'd like to talk about what happened after I found out Dan had died."

The next week, Sarah was excited to tell us she and Rick had sold their house and would be moving in the next few months. Beth and Caroline offered to help with the move and settling into their new home. Sarah's excitement was contagious, but Beth could tell Sarah was anxious to finish telling them what happened after the phone call.

"I was shaking badly when I heard the message. I couldn't even respond to what I had heard. I don't remember collapsing, but suddenly found myself sitting on the floor. I had the phone in my hand but don't remember how I ended up on the floor. I started to rip the curlers out of my hair as I raced down the stairs. I was screaming hysterically! My mother was in the kitchen cooking dinner. I don't recall where my brother and sister were, but my screams alerted my mother and I remember that she walked into the living room at the same time as I did. My father was sitting in the living room reading the newspaper and gave little indication that his daughter was screaming uncontrollably.

"I was aware that I was shouting incoherently. I remember my father standing up and appearing unsure of how to react. If anything, he seemed angered by my screams, perhaps having been startled and interrupted. I started to scream hysterically, 'Dan is dead! He's dead!!' I felt a total loss as to what to do. My father lost his patience and in desperation said, 'Get a grip on yourself.' A reaction like that from my father was not unexpected and I knew there would be little compassion from either of my parents. My mother stood silently in the doorway. Deep down, I knew there was little they could do, and looking back, I can appreciate that neither of them were capable of dealing with this sort of crisis. I was standing in the living room crying uncontrollably, but neither reached out to give me a hug or even touch me.

"I returned to the safety of my room. The phone rang immediately. It was Emma who had heard the news and offered to come pick me up. I knew I had to get through supper pretending that I 'had gotten a grip on myself' before my parents would let me go out. At the supper table, I asked them if I could go out with Emma for the evening. They asked where I was going and I answered a bunch of friends were going bowling. I was given permission to go and couldn't wait until Emma got to my house. As soon as I stepped into Emma's car, I collapsed in huge gulps of sobs."

"Thank goodness you had Emma, Sarah." Beth whispered.

"The bowling alley was packed with Dan's and my friends all looking to console each other and cry together. It was like a gathering for Dan. We were all in shock seeking believable explanations from each other. How could this happen? How could he have had a heart attack? Weren't heart attacks just for old people? No one was supposed to die when they were only seventeen. It was as though we were holding our own calling hours to celebrate Dan's life except that being the first time any of us had experienced a loss of this magnitude, we could do nothing more than hug and console each other. We clung to each other, even students who were essentially strangers from other 'groups' as we were all temporarily connected in our grief and bewilderment. I had to excuse myself often to go to the ladies' room where I could cry hysterically.

"At the end of the evening, Emma drove me home and I cried myself to sleep. I felt such a huge loss; cheated that I had never had the chance to let Dan know how important he was to me. I felt such extreme guilt and couldn't get rid of the thought 'Dan died thinking I didn't care or love him'. I was haunted.

"On Saturday morning, Dan's parents called me and asked if I could come to their house. My parents let me take the car and I drove to Dan's home not sure why they wanted to see me but glad that I was going to spend time with them, to be near Dan vicariously through his parents. When I walked in the door, his mother grabbed me and hugged me as though I was her lifeline and she was afraid to let go. Perhaps she felt as I, that I was a part of Dan's life and she wanted to be close to me. We clung to each other, crying together, yet neither one of us was able to ease each other's pain. Dan's father stood up from the couch and came over to join us. He too hugged me while I continued to cry. His mother took a step back, looked at me and evidently, needing assurance, simply asked, 'He was a good boy, wasn't he?' I wasn't quite sure what she was asking, I assured her that, 'Yes he was a very good boy…the very best.'

"Instead of calling hours, Dan's parents arranged a memorial service on Monday morning. They shared that Dan had died of a heart attack brought on by heart damage from rheumatic fever he had contracted when he was three years old; damage that had never been identified or suspected by anyone. I spent the day with Dan's family not wanting to leave, feeling comfort by just being with them in their home; knowing I was bringing them comfort as well, and recognizing there would be little or none offered at my home. For most of the weekend, I spent as much time as I was allowed on the phone seeking solace, comfort and relief from my grief from my friends.

"On Saturday, as soon as I reached home from Dan's house, I explained to my parents that there would be a service on Monday and asked my parents for permission to attend the service. I was told arrangements had been made for me to return to college on Sunday at the end of the holiday weekend as I was expected back on campus by Sunday night. I begged. I cried. The thought that I would not be allowed to attend Dan's service with our friends was beyond my comprehension."

"Why weren't they going to let you go? Didn't they realize how much you were hurting?"

"I begged them, Beth. I told them I needed to be there. There was no way they would understand my guilt or all the feelings I was having so I just gave them a bunch of reasons like 'everyone else but me is going'. They finally gave in.

"It was a beautiful day on Monday; much too lovely a day to be saying goodbye to a young man, my friend I loved. The service was held at a large white Congregational Church. The pews were filled with family and close friends. His family asked me to sit with them, but I thanked them and said I would sit up in the balcony with our friends and the faculty from the school. The service seemed to be over before it had begun. We gathered outside after the service at the doorway to the church where everyone was hugging. One person after another approached me to offer condolences and either hugged me or squeezed my hand.

"I felt such tremendous physical pain in my chest that I had difficulty even opening my arms to embrace them; I felt I needed to embrace myself. I needed to wrap my arms around me and hold on to myself as tightly as I could. I was consumed with grief and have no recollection of where I went after the service. I remember approaching Dan's parents and his three sisters to receive a last hug. I never saw any of them again.

"On Tuesday, my father drove me to the station where I would travel by train to a station about an hour from the college campus. My father had arranged a taxi to pick me up at the station and drive me to college; it was after midnight when I arrived back on campus. Despite the hour, there was a buzz in the dormitory when I walked in. The news had preceded my arrival. Over the weekend I had telephoned my roommate to let her know I wasn't returning on Sunday and why which she had shared with the others in the dorm. I was greeted by her and others with warm, welcoming hugs which I was only slightly able to return. I was still too numb with remorse and guilt to feel any comfort.

"Students in other dorms on campus had no idea who I was but on Wednesday I overheard students talking, 'Did you hear about one of the students? Her boyfriend dropped dead on Friday.' That was how I came to be identified. I was the student whose boyfriend had died suddenly on Friday. I attended class but that was all. I sat in class but couldn't respond. I had withdrawn behind a wall of pain, guilt and shock.

"As soon as I returned to campus, I called Jake and explained to him that I would not be able to attend the dance with him the following weekend and why. He was irritated with my explanation and essentially said with feeling, 'If this Dan meant that much to you, there's no reason for us to continue seeing each other.' I didn't care."

"I can understand why you couldn't go to that dance, Sarah. I wouldn't have been able to go, either. It seems to me that if Jake couldn't understand that, he was insensitive and not someone you most likely would have been happy with in the long run," Caroline noted.

"The day after the dance, my mother called and wanted to hear all about the dance. Had I had a good time? What did the decorations look like? Did everyone like my dress? How was the band? I lied through the whole conversation using my imagination to answer her questions as I didn't have the heart to disappoint her. She had been so excited about the dress we had found and excited about the dance. I couldn't hurt her and tell her I had never gone to the dance. I knew she wouldn't understand. I rambled on about how great the band was, and told her the dress was a huge success. I said I was the bell of the ball! I didn't tell her I never wore the dress. I didn't wear it that night or ever."

"Sarah, you did the right thing in not telling your mother. She might have understood, but she might have been hurt and what purpose did the truth serve?" Beth said.

Caroline agreed and added, "It would have been terrible to ruin her joy after having found the dress with you."

"Within two weeks, I was called to the Office of the Dean where I sat across from her at her desk. She asked, 'Is there anything I could do to help? Your professors have reported that they're concerned about you. I understand you're not completing your assignments. Your grades are falling."

"I didn't have any idea what to say to the Dean. How was I supposed to explain to someone like the Dean that I was filled with guilt and sorrow? I assured her that I was fine; it was just an adjustment. I confessed that I was trying to get through each day but was having trouble concentrating on my work. The Dean was sympathetic but told me she had to follow the rules. Because of my failing grades, I was placed on academic probation and not allowed to leave the dorm on weekends. I was offered academic support by the college but that wasn't what I needed. It never occurred to me to ask to see the school psychologist. It was only a few more days later when I called the church and asked to meet with the pastor. I know I told you about that before. I struggled through the remainder of the year, determined to just get through the school year. I took one day at a time. Since I was on academic probation, I was grounded on campus oftentimes alone on weekends as my friends went off to their mixers and social events. Although I occasionally got bored on the weekends, I didn't care to go to the mixers, anyway. That was the last thing I wanted. The thought of trying to be social, cheerful and animated was more than I could muster.

"The entire year I cheered myself on internally to get through the day as each day became a little easier for me. I knew I needed something to distract me. I started to knit. Knitting kept my fingers moving and occupied my time. It was soothing and the feel of the yarn against my hands brought me comfort. Just like both of you have talked about, I didn't care what I knit. I just knit.

"I had shut myself out from the world but I let God in. Prayer helped and kept me focused on trusting something else to ease my pain – a higher power. He helped. I noticed each day became a little less painful than the one before. I started to forgive myself and trust my faith; choosing to believe that Dan left the earth, as excited as I had been about seeing each other that night. I chose to and so needed to believe that he knew at the end how special he was to me and would have convinced me that night not to feel guilty. That was the type of young man he was. He would have gladly forgiven me if we had seen each other that night and would have wanted me to forgive myself."

"I know you never saw Dan again, Sarah, but you said you spoke with him on the phone on Wednesday, so

I'm sure he knew how you felt about him. I really think he knew, Sarah. Please forgive yourself," Caroline pleaded

"I never went to another mixer nor did I date anyone the rest of the school year. I returned home for the summer in June and rekindled my friendships with my friends – minus one. My faithful friends were a tremendous support and I leaned on them. I had taken a part-time job working four hours in the morning typing a manuscript for a book. When not working, I spent my afternoons at the community pool, often knitting even in the sun. Toward the end of the summer, one of the lifeguards approached me and expressed his condolences for my loss. He introduced himself as Rick, although I already knew his name. He then asked if I was interested in perhaps going to a movie some time. I had started to let go of some of my grief. I knew I would never forget Dan but I knew I had to begin to move on. I told him that I would enjoy going to a movie sometime. He assured me he would call. I thought to myself, when one door closes, another seems to open, at least partially."

"From how you have described Dan's family, I'll bet he was raised in a loving family and would have wanted you to be happy, Sarah. I'm sure he would not have wanted you to spend the rest of your life feeling guilty. So, you met your husband Rick not long after Dan died?"

Sarah and Caroline looked across the room at Beth, recognizing that her expression was soulful.

"Beth, is everything okay?" Caroline asked.

"Yes, I'm alright," Beth answered. "It's just hearing Sarah talk about Dan's death and the sadness brought back some memories of that night in the hospital when I wasn't sure if I was going to die or what was going to happen to me in the future."

Caroline asked, "Do you want to talk about it, Beth?"

Beth nodded. "Throughout the entire night, I was aware of nurses moving in and out of my room. I was aware of being poked, prodded, the humming of machines, the banging of doors, the beeping of other machines in the hall, the murmuring of voices. Morning arrived at last. I opened my eyes from a semi-stupor state to realize that I was still in bed which was being wheeled down the hall again. I was returned to an operating room where my doctor greeted me with a smile and squeeze of my hand. He assured me convincingly I was going to be alright. I was given more sedation and again shut my eyes from the glare of the bright lights overhead.

"I was barely alert, but was told that the doctor would remove the internal packing to determine if the internal bleeding had stopped and evaluate further the damage to my body. There was no pain. I again felt nothing –physically or emotionally, inside or out. I was 'being done to' and that was how I survived alone. Even in my half-conscious state, I was steeling myself, building internal strength and resolve, trying to hang on to my sanity and mind. Even with the sedation, I was shutting down inside – my heart – my soul – my whole being. I was aware that the doctor was performing some medical procedure and just before I nodded off again, I heard the doctor say with relief, 'It worked. She's going to make it. Take her back to her room and give her a baked potato.'"

"Are you joking, Beth? Was he kidding?" Caroline questioned.

"No. Those were his words and I remember hearing the relief and joy in his voice. A day later, I was moved from ICU to a regular room where I remained for two weeks having lost so much blood that I was weak and unable to get out of bed. I spent the time watching people pass by my door. I saw women shuffling up and down the halls. I stared out the window next to my bed and wondered if the numbness I felt inside would ever go away.

"One day, I heard one woman say to another as they walked by my door, 'I wonder why they don't ever bring a baby to that girl?' I wondered about my baby. I knew it was a boy and I knew he weighed ten pounds. I knew he was within a few feet from my door but I couldn't get there. I wasn't sure I wanted to. I felt nothing. I felt no connection at that time to the baby or to another human being – even life. I was alive but without life. I was waiting for everything to be over. Ellen and John never asked or mentioned seeing the baby, nor did I. Years later, Ellen told me that my father said I was not to be allowed to see the baby. 'Your father thought it would be easier for you in the long run,' Ellen said. At the time, I didn't question his order."

"Are you sorry you didn't walk down the hall to the nursery?"

"Sarah, sometimes I think so, but I can't imagine seeing my baby and never being able to hold him or see him again. I was in enough pain. I guess, looking back, my father was probably right."

"A week later, the medical staff determined that I was strong enough to try and get out of bed and begin to build my strength. With a nurse on either side for support, I was helped out of bed to stand and immediately collapsed in a heap on the floor – my legs unable to hold me up. I was not allowed out of bed for another few days until this time I was strong enough to hold myself up and take a few steps. I was encouraged to get up as often as I could but, never alone, walk around the room or down the hall but never in the direction of the nursery. I slept most days. It was quiet without visitors and alone in my single room. After ten days, I was released from the hospital and able to go back to Ellen and John's to recover for another week until my imaginary vacation at the house on the lake was over and I would leave. And all that time, what did I want more than anything? To be with Jack, to see him, to have him hold me, to put his arms around me, support me, be there for me – to tell me I was not alone. I wanted to lean on him.

"The last few days in Illinois were spent in preparation for my 're-entry' into the real world. Ellen helped me gather the few things I would take home with me. I had lost over thirty- five pounds and my little over five feet tall frame was almost scrawny. I was a shadow of the girl I had been when I had left home six months earlier. I was four sizes smaller which meant all of my clothes hung on me. Ellen took me shopping for a few new outfits, some things at least to get me home. To the world, I looked like a young girl in a new dress ready to travel home. What no one could detect was the extent of emotional damage.

"Alone in the house, while Ellen ran to the grocery store, I gathered all the 'scarves' I had knit and carelessly rolled them up, stuffed them in a large plastic bag and tied the top of the bag. I carried the bag down the flight of stairs to the dumpster in the parking lot behind the building. Even though I can't remember the colors of the yarn, I recall, as though it was yesterday, my feeling as I dropped that bag of scarves into the dumpster. To my mind, it symbolized the end of that part of my life. The knitted 'scarves' had served their purpose. I no longer needed them and certainly didn't want them as a reminder. It was time to move on.

"The fear of the flight home loomed over me as I got ready to leave. I had never flown and was terrified of heights since the age of ten when my parents, insisting as part of my well-rounded exposure and growth, signed me up for swimming lessons; one requirement included I jump off the high board. As I stood on the end of that board, the water came rushing up at me and I lost all sense of balance and perspective. There was no railing to hold on to. I dropped to my knees, crawled out on the board, and rolled off the edge closing my eyes so the pool surface rushing up at me was hidden from view. I was terrified at the thought of being in an airplane, high off the ground…alone."

Caroline and Sarah moved over to sit on either side of Beth as her words rushed out in torrents, painting a palpable picture of her fear.

"John and Ellen helped me to the boarding gate where my bag was checked in. I remember carrying a small potted plant but have forgotten why or its significance. At least it was alive. I certainly wasn't. Perhaps this was a plant I had been given as a gift for my room or had been gifted to me while in the hospital. Maybe it was something alive to bridge the span of one home to the other.

"The plane took off. I had never experienced anything like the sensation. I was suddenly thrown back on that diving board, the water surging toward me. I felt helpless. The feeling of weakness in my knees, the fluttering in the pit of my stomach quickly became waves of nausea.

"The flight seemed endless; only three hours in the air seemed like three days. I knew my parents were meeting me in New York and that compounded the anxiety. I had not seen them in many months and I feared their reaction toward me. They had told my brother and sister that they were driving my mother to the New York airport and she was flying to Illinois to pick me up. It was to be a contrived surprise for everyone that I would be getting off the plane.

"As the plane landed, I couldn't look. I had been praying the entire time, the same prayer over and over for three hours. I wanted to believe that if I had survived a night of near death a month ago, I could survive a plane ride. God had saved me once; I had faith He would save me again despite the fact that one of His spokesmen had told me I was going to burn in Hell for my sins.

"I lined up in the aisle with the other passengers to get off the plane. I couldn't get off that plane fast enough. The plane was resting on the tarmac rather than at a jetway but I made it down the stairs, holding the railing with my free hand while my other clutched the potted plant. As soon as my feet touched the ground, I lost it. I became hysterical. The months of abandonment, fear, shame, guilt, remorse came rushing at me. I couldn't stop crying. I was blinded by my tears rolling down my face. I thought I was following the stream of fellow passengers heading toward the terminal; however, I was crying so hard, I lost my way. I'm not sure how I got separated from the rest of the passengers, but I got confused and didn't know where I was, still holding my potted plant, gripping it as though it held meaning to me – as though it was the anchor to the life I had been living for six months; the only living thing I was bringing home.

"I suddenly was in a building with planes, parts of planes, lots of men standing around in coveralls and uniforms. All the noise stopped. I was aware that everyone was staring at me. I didn't know where I was. I began to panic. I was still crying so hard that my tears were dripping onto the front of my new dress. I clutched my plant. I heard shouting and loud voices of men. I still didn't know where I was. I just knew that everyone around me was in a work uniform and a few men were walking toward me. There were many tools lying around and then the loud noises of machines started again. Standing still, I felt someone touch my arm. A man stood beside me and took my hand. I had no idea how I had gotten where I was other than I was blind and wandering aimlessly trying to find my way back out. He gently led me slowly to the doorway of a building which I later learned was an airplane hangar and walked with me across the tarmac to the terminal building"

"As soon as I entered the terminal, I saw my parents, brother and sister standing together. I heard my parents shout 'Surprise' letting my brother and sister know that they were coming to New York to pick me up not to take my mother to the airport. Once again, I played along with the fantasy pretending this time to be excited. One more lie added to my life of lies. I stood with head bent, crying uncontrollably as my father approached me, gave me a hug and simply said, 'Rough flight, huh?' My mother was silent as she gave me a hug."

"Did you expect a different kind of greeting from your family, Beth?" Caroline asked.

"I don't know. I was so nervous I didn't know what to expect from them and I'm guessing they were as nervous as I was and probably didn't know how to react.

"The ride home took two hours. I was given the honor of sitting in the front seat between my parents, my brother and sister in the back seat. My brother and sister asked me a few questions as my parents spoke as though I had just returned from the 'time of my life'. They asked about the weather at the lake where I had vacationed for two weeks. Did we swim a lot? What kinds of things did we do besides swimming? Wow, didn't I look great! I stared straight ahead. I answered their questions but was struggling with re-entry' fighting the urge to remain within my own silent world. Their questions were forcing me to be alert, on target, careful to remember the lies, be communicative. I knew within hours I would be expected to resume my life as I had known it before. Life marched on. No one could relate to the trauma I had experienced.

"On the first night of my return, there was a party at the home of a friend. It was only because of my extreme need to see my friends that I was able to drum up the courage to ask my parents if I could go. I was shocked that they said I could. I couldn't wait to get there. I wanted nothing more than to resume my life, reconnect with my support system, see and be near Jack. Jane picked me up and hugged me with joy to have her best friend back.

"Within minutes of walking in the door to the party, it was as though an invisible cord connected Jack and me. In the crowded room I was able to spot him immediately talking to a group of fellow football players on the other side of the room. He looked up as though he too sensed my presence as soon as I walked in. I took a deep breath and struggled to keep from crying; I fought to hold on to the iron shield masking my pain. I did not want to cry. I was determined that I would appear strong and confident letting everyone note I was back and life was better than ever.

"My heart raced as he walked across the room and opened his arms, hugging me. I put my arms around him, savoring the few minutes of the closeness I had wanted and needed for months. He stepped back and with compassion asked, 'Are you okay? My mother said you had some trouble.' I quickly, perhaps too quickly answered, 'Yes, I'm fine.' No one would know, certainly not Jack. He would be the last one to know my pain. He had abandoned me. He ran away leaving me to face everyone – alone. He had continued to finish his high school year when he had returned five months after running away. His life, for all practical purposes, was normal. He had been able to continue playing sports, studying, going to parties, even the prom. Never would I let him know how much he had hurt me or the extent of my pain. Years later, Jane would share her perspective with me about my return. She described me as a girl who had returned a shell of her former self; someone who lacked enthusiasm, laughter, a spark for life. Looking at my high school yearbook picture supported her impression. There was no smile. My eyes were dark. I was brooding, indeed, a shell of a seventeen-year-old girl with a lovely smile now seldom seen.

"I can't imagine how you must have felt to finally see Jack. I feel as though I could cry just picturing him walking across the room to hug you after what you'd been through," Caroline said, giving Beth a hug.

"Many friends came up to me throughout the evening to hug me while politely asking about the school I had attended. Had I met many friends? Was I planning on going back to Illinois in September? Was I just home for the summer? At the end of the party, Jack came over to me, squeezed my hand and said goodnight. It was the last substantive gesture or connection we would have for two years. I once again turned to knitting to relieve stress together with a sense of purpose despite the fact that it mattered not what I was knitting. Knitting kept my fingers busy; knit one, purl one."

When Beth finished, Caroline commented. "I think you were so brave, Beth, to go to that party. I can understand how anxious you were to see Jack, but to put yourself right out with your peers on your first night home, especially after that airport experience, I think is remarkable."

Sarah, sobbing added, "My heart is breaking just thinking of how you must have felt when he hugged you. I would have cried."

Thanksgiving was coming up the following week, so the ladies ended the night by opting to skip the next Wednesday night but agreed they had much to be thankful for – having found each other and the friendships they were building.

When the week after Thanksgiving arrived, each admitted they relished the time with family but yearned for the return of their Wednesday night gathering and night out. Not long after settling into their chairs in the familiarity of the loft, Caroline said there had been an incident with Steve over the holiday weekend which had brought back bad memories of other incidents with him.

"After the night Steve disappeared, things were fairly quiet, but I admit I was guarded. I just was never sure when I would return home and find him gone again. There was no further disappearance though and I started to relax. Steve's business was doing well and required little of his time or effort. All was well at my work.

"On the first weekend of May, we traditionally spent the weekend getting the boat ready to put in the water. Last May we were scraping and painting the hull when Steve's daughter came over to tell us she was excited to participate in a sailboat race sponsored by a renowned sailing organization. The race would last two weeks and sail from Venezuela through Sint Maarten to Portland, Maine. Steve and I told her we would come and say goodbye before she flew to Venezuela in another week to meet the others in the race. When we arrived a week later, she was typically dressed in her grubby clothes and covered with dirt from cleaning the deck of a boat she was preparing for launch. We talked to her for a while, offered to take her to supper which she refused; 'No time', she said. She was anxious to finish her work. I gave her a warm hug and told her we'd love to hear all about her adventure when she returned. She went to give Steve a hug but dressed in his good clothes, he put his hands up indicating that he didn't want to get his clean shirt dirty. He blew her a kiss.

"The following weekend, the weather on Saturday was not good and we opted out of a sail and stayed home. At the end of the afternoon, we were surprised and pleased to receive a call from Steve's daughter who was in Sint Maarten where they had anchored for the night to restock supplies for the second leg of the race. Her exuberance reverberated through the phone lines. She looked forward to the second part of the race and had decided to change ships for the second half to take advantage of the varied experience on a different type of ship. She said she would see us in a week, blew a kiss, and told her dad she loved him. On Sunday, we awakened to a beautiful day and decided to go for a day sail. We arrived back home around six o'clock and had just finished unpacking the car when the phone rang.

"Steve answered and I heard him ask, 'Does her mother know?' My first thought was that the call was telling us our terminally ill sister-in-law had passed away.

"I heard Steve end the conversation and then a loud crash. I turned around and watched in horror as Steve pounded his fist with such force against the wooden hallway door that a panel shattered into splinters. I ran into the hall asking what had happened. Not in my wildest imagination did I suspect the call was about his daughter. He didn't answer. He just walked down the hall and lay on the bed staring at the ceiling."

"Who was on the phone, Caroline?" Sarah wanted to know.

"The call had been from a representative of the organization which had sponsored the sailing event, calling to tell Steve that there had been an accident on one of the ships. The two ships had no sooner left Sint Maarten for the second leg of the race when a strong wind hit one of the ships causing high waves, and one of the ships went down. The ship that sank was the ship his daughter had been on with eighteen others. The caller went on to say there were some survivors but that Steve's daughter had not yet been found. He offered encouragement that the Coast Guard was continuing to search the area."

"Oh my God, Caroline, what did you do?" Sarah asked.

"We didn't know who to call or what to do but agreed sitting home waiting wasn't an option. I called my office to let them know I would not be in for a few days then called the airlines to book a flight to Sint Maarten to depart the next morning. At the airport, we met a man whose wife had been on the same ship as Steve's daughter. We exchanged information but neither of us knew anything more than what we had been told the previous night. Somehow the airline was aware that there were three passengers on their flight who were awaiting word of any further survivors. The pilot monitored information during the flight which he relayed via the flight attendant to the three of us. The information never changed. The message was always the same – no further survivors had been found as yet.

"We landed in Sint Maarten and were immediately taken to the Coast Guard in Simpson Bay. We were ushered into a large room crowded with adults and teenagers – some parents obviously anxiously awaiting word of their loved ones, and young men and women about the age of Steve's daughter. By their appearance and dress, it was evident these were some of the survivors. I had taken only a few steps into the room when a young man I'd never seen before walked up to me and threw his arms around me. Holding on to me with all his strength, he sobbed uncontrollably on my shoulder. I held him as tightly as I could, not understanding why I had been singled out by this young stranger. As he hugged me, he said, 'I was supposed to be on that boat too. I feel so guilty that I wasn't there with my brother. I don't understand why I was saved and my brother is lost.'"

"Oh, that poor kid," Beth commented.

"We were all quieted by an officer behind a large desk who gave us an update that essentially offered no additional information. I inquired why someone or the Coast Guard couldn't locate the sunken ship and raise it. I was told that the Coast Guard knew where it was, but the depth of the water made it impossible to do anything. We were assured that the Coast Guard would continue their search until such time it was deemed no more survivors would be found.

"The island opened its hearts to us. All the flags on island were lowered to half-mast as hotels and private residents opened their doors to us for accommodation. Each of the three days brought less hope. Steve and I walked to the beach and the harbor where the ship had departed that Sunday morning and from where we had received the last call from his daughter. It helped to know that she had stood on the same ground where we were standing; it was as close as we could get to her – a symbolic bond to where she had spent her last few moments on land. It was where we had last heard her voice, where we had said our goodbye. We looked at the sea and saw it through a different lens- not a Caribbean turquoise blue. At that time, the sea held no beauty. It was dark, evil, cold."

"How long did you stay there, Caroline?" Sarah asked.

"We only stayed a few days hoping we would be there when Steve's daughter was found but three days later it was evident there would be no more survivors. We returned home and tried to pick up our life, but it held a dark shadow. There was a void. We had no desire to sail. In fact, Steve decided he wanted to sell the boat-it was too much of a reminder. The circumstances of Steve's daughter's death made it difficult for closure. There was no body to bury. There would be no funeral. Steve's first wife decided on a memorial service at sea. A month later, we gathered by the ocean where we held a brief memorial, shared two readings from the Bible and placed a wreath at water's edge to be carried out to sea. It didn't seem to be enough but there was nothing else to be done except allow time to heal the void and loss.

"A month later I answered the phone and was told by a young man that he was sailing with Steve's daughter when their ship sank. He had been rescued by the Coast Guard a week after the sinking and had survived for almost a week by holding onto a piece of wood. He had been badly stung by jellyfish and suffered from dehydration, but after two weeks in the hospital had recovered – at least physically. He explained it was important for him to talk to us as he had been with Steve's daughter when the ship sank. He wanted us to know that it was four o'clock in the morning when Steve's daughter had just ended her watch and gone down below. The wind came out of nowhere and was so powerful that it hit the ship which began to immediately list and take on water. He explained Steve's daughter was at the foot of the ladder, preparing to climb out of the hatch to go back on deck, when she noticed her shipmate carrying her young child. Steve's daughter stepped aside to let the woman and baby go up first, but the water rushed into the hatch with such force that the young man said none of them had a chance against the force. They were all forced back inside with no possibility of escape. The only survivors were those who were on deck.

"I thanked him for the call and felt a sense of apprehension as I knew I had to relate the phone call to Steve when he came home from town. It was as though he sensed when he walked through the door that something had happened. Perhaps he read my expression. I asked him to sit with me on the couch as I shared the latest news. It was the final chapter, and while it brought closure, it didn't ease the pain or fill the void."

"My gosh! How did Steve react? He must have been in such pain."

"Beth, he just stared at me with that same look he would get in his eyes when he talked about his time at the private school. Maybe that was how he escaped the pain of the moment. He just stood up and went to lie down on our bed.

"I went back to work and immersed myself in projects. My friend suggested knitting was a good way to relieve the stress and I took it up with such energy I couldn't stop. I knit sweaters for everyone. I knit argyle socks. When I got bored with just straight knitting, I challenged myself with Irish cable knit sweaters for everyone. I grew to depend on my needles to calm my nerves.

"A month after the loss of Steve's daughter, just weeks ago, I got home from work to find him gone again. I didn't panic as much as I had the first time because I knew he would be calling and assure me he was alright. There had been another disappearance last year when my daughter visited. She and I had gone to a movie and returned home around ten o'clock. We walked in the back-kitchen door to find raw eggs smashed on the walls and floor, the chandelier suspended over the kitchen table hanging by a single wire, and the distinct smell of beer. My daughter incredulously asked, 'Oh my God. Who could have done this?' and I was forced to confess that I was living with a deeply troubled man. I blamed his behavior on the loss of his daughter because I wasn't ready to let my secret out that there had been a few incidents of unusual behavior prior to her death or that Steve drank too much and seemed to have some psychological issues. Steve didn't return that night but, by that point, I had grown accustomed somewhat to his routine and minimized it to my daughter. I went to bed and assured her that all was well and he would return in a day or so.

"Right before I met both of you, I had another meeting in the evening and walked in the house shortly after nine. Out of habit, I walked to the bathroom and made note that the shaving kit was on the vanity, but clearly Steve was not home. I opened the refrigerator to get some juice and saw a case of beer, which was unusual. Never before had I seen a case of beer in the refrigerator. I waited for about an hour for him to return, but when he wasn't home by eleven, I got into bed and began to fall asleep.

"I was just dozing off when the room was suddenly filled with light. I heard Steve walk in the room but couldn't see him because there was a short hallway to our first-floor bedroom. As soon as he came into view, I could tell right away he had been drinking. He started to yell but I couldn't understand what he was saying. He was very drunk. I quickly sat up feeling I would be less vulnerable sitting up than lying down. He stood beside my small 19thC pine bureau just inside the doorway and with one swipe of his hand, threw it crashing to the floor. I sat stunned. I was terrified. I was shaking and didn't dare move. I didn't dare try to intervene or speak. I was afraid if I uttered a sound it would provoke Steve further."

"Oh my God, Caroline. Had he ever hurt you before? Are there things you're not telling us? Were you ever physically abused?" Sarah prodded.

"No. He turned and left the room without a word. I heard the sound of heavy thumping of his boots going up the stairs to the den where there was a television. I breathed a sigh of relief but didn't dare lie down. I didn't dare leave. I didn't know what to do. When I didn't hear his thumping on the stairs again, I assumed that he had decided to sleep upstairs on the couch. I was greatly relieved and actually sank back down in the bed pulling the covers up to my chin as though they could provide me protection. I had never encountered anything like this before.

"I don't think I dozed off as I was on alert, but perhaps I had been praying for comfort when about thirty minutes later, I again heard Steve's footsteps stomping on the stairs. This time his stomping sounded different, though, and I could tell that he'd continued down the cellar stairs located just outside our bedroom door off the kitchen. I had no idea what he was doing or why he was going into the cellar, but didn't dare shout out and ask. I thought if he thought I was sleeping; I would be safer.

"Within minutes, I heard the loud crashing of wood and metal accompanied by primal screams unlike anything I'd ever heard before. I was frightened and angry; and maybe that's what gave me the courage to get out of bed. Whatever possessed me to venture down the cellar stairs is beyond me although for some reason I thought I had the power to calm him. I thought I could talk some reason into him. I knew he was still grief stricken and again I excused his behavior, at the least minimized it. I was tired and my fear turned to near rage. I stormed out of bed livid and determined to bring an end to this episode. I had been exhausted but was now fueled with nervous energy."

"Gosh, Caroline. I can't believe you went down there. I don't think I would have done that. I would have grabbed the phone and called the police." Beth confessed.

"As I got to the third step from the bottom of the cellar stairway, I looked over to see that Steve had an ax in his hand. He was swinging it haphazardly in every direction. He'd already smashed the ping pong table to splinters and destroyed the shelves holding numerous gallons of paint which were now lying open on the floor. Paint was spattered everywhere. I found the courage to speak. I gently said, 'Come on, Steve. Come to bed.' I had no sooner finished when he looked up and realized I was at the foot of the stairs. He ran around what was left of the ping pong table and lunged toward me wielding the ax. I turned and ran up the stairs, slammed the cellar door hoping to slow him down, grabbed my coat, boots and purse on the chair in the kitchen and ran as fast as I could out the back door to my car in the driveway. It was midnight."

When Caroline finished speaking, Beth and Sarah were in shock, unable to speak. Their facial expressions spoke volumes.

"Is this the same night you talked a little about when you said Steve was sick and ended up in the hospital?" Beth asked, starting to put pieces of the story together.

"Yes, but I didn't want to tell you the whole story that night. I was embarrassed." Caroline answered.

"It was cold and I had no idea where to go. All I knew was that it wasn't safe in my house. I had to get out. I was dressed in my pajamas which I had covered with a coat. I had thin boots on without socks and I was cold. I had the heat turned up to high in the car but it wasn't helping. I drove around town for an hour or so before pulling into the parking lot of Dunkin Donuts. It was almost one-thirty in the morning and I can't imagine what the young man behind the counter thought when I walked in to get a cup of tea at that hour looking as I did. I was looking totally wrinkled as though I had just gotten out of bed! I took the tea to the car and sipped it slowly while I held the cup to warm my hands. I had nowhere else to go. When I finished, I started to drive around again.

"Our house was on a very short street which could be accessed from either direction and I could see the house from either side street. I drove around for a while and could watch what was happening at the house. Were the lights off? Was Steve's car still in the driveway? Did it look like it was safe to go home? I drove this route for another hour until I glanced to see three police cars parked in front."

"You must have panicked!" Sarah said.

"I had no idea why there were police cars at the curb. I immediately turned into my street and pulled up behind one of the police cars. An officer approached the car and shining a flashlight in my face as I rolled down my window, asked, 'What is your name?' I could barely give him my name when he asked what I was doing here. I didn't know how to answer. I told him I lived here and thought he must think I'm crazy to be driving around town at that hour. He asked where I had been. I suspect he knew why I was out in the middle of the night and was just looking for affirmation. I don't remember what I said but I knew I couldn't tell him the truth. How could I tell him I had to run for my life from my house for fear of being killed by my husband? I merely told the officer with a very brave voice, 'I have to go into my house; that's my husband in there.'

The officer didn't react but asked if my husband had been having some problems lately to which I responded that he had lost his daughter a few months earlier and hadn't been quite right since. I didn't know what to say and that was the best I could come up with. He seemed to accept my response."

"Why didn't you tell the officer the truth? He could have helped you." Sarah asked.

"I was afraid to tell him. I was afraid of people finding out the truth of what my life with Steve was like, not knowing what they would do to him. I was afraid they would take him away. I just wanted to smooth it all and make it sound like it was no big deal.

"I opened my car door and stepped out on to the road. The officer put out his arm to block me and told me in no uncertain terms, 'You're not going in there.' I emphatically told him I was at which point he told me to stand still and not move."

Caroline had to interrupt. "Weren't you terrified, Sarah? What was going through your mind?"

"Oh my God, Caroline. I had no idea what to think. I just felt the urgency to get inside and make everything better.

"I had never experienced anything like this before. The policeman called someone on his walkie-talkie who turned out to be another officer in the house. I heard the officer standing beside me say, 'I've got the wife out here and she wants to come in'. I then heard a response, 'She can't come in alone. Bring her in but you stay with her and don't let her near her husband.'

"I couldn't imagine what I would find when I walked in the door. The officer who had met me in the street shielded me from Steve as we entered the room through the back door. I had to look. I saw Steve standing in one corner of the kitchen leaning on the counters, penned in by two other officers. As the officer and I side-stepped through the kitchen, we passed into the hall and into the living room. Steve, obviously drunk, started to scream obscenities at me calling me awful names as I moved through the room. The police tried to calm him to no avail. He kept screaming and my bodyguard urged me to keep moving as quickly as possible."

"Why was he screaming at you? What had you done wrong? Didn't you say you were just late at work because of a meeting?"

"I did, Sarah, but my husband was ill and not rational."

"There were pills and broken glass scattered everywhere, covering the counters randomly and strewn across the floor. The house smelled of turpentine and paint. My uniformed bodyguard moved with me farther into the living room as far across the room from the kitchen entrance as possible. One of the three policemen in the kitchen came into the living room and asked me if I knew what the pills were in the cupboard. I explained they were probably my thyroid pills and I didn't know what else might be up there in the cupboard – maybe some old diet pills.

"Through the thin walls, I heard the two officers in the kitchen trying to calm my husband. Steve would have none of it and continued to swear at me, calling me filthy names, yelling that he hoped I rotted in Hell. I leaned on the mantel for support with my elbows so I could cover my ears with my hands. Nothing stifled the tirade or even the calming voices of the officers. I could hear every word. After what seemed like a very long time and numerous attempts by the police to calm him, I heard one officer say to the other, 'Okay. Let's take him.' I squeezed my hands harder over my ears but the noise was so loud it barely muffled the sounds from the kitchen.

"There was screaming, the sound of flesh hitting flesh, the sound of wrestling, grunting, and groans. As Steve struggled against the three officers, the sounds of their scuffle painted a picture in my mind that I can still see. I knew they were wrestling with him and he was fighting back. I knew he was being beaten up. I started to cry.

"The officer standing with me told me they had called for an ambulance. The yelling continued as I heard them take Steve, kicking and screaming, out the back door and watched out the window as they strapped him on a gurney in a strait jacket and placed him in the ambulance. Outside, the sirens were deafening in the stillness of the night, but inside the house it was suddenly eerily silent.

"I walked into the kitchen and sat down in shock. I wanted to rush to neaten up the mess and erase the visible reminder of my nightmare. The policemen asked me a few questions which I did my best to answer. I explained about the death of Steve's daughter and his grief. I was confused as to how they had come to the house until one officer explained that my husband had panicked, called the police after taking pills in the cupboard, and phoned 911. As the officers got ready to leave, one officer advised me to leave the house because of the fumes from the basement. That was when I called my friend, Ann, and then the phone rang and it was the hospital."

"Did you ever find out why the woman from the hospital was yelling at you on the phone?"

"Beth, I think they were frustrated with dealing with Steve and even though they had tied him down, they couldn't stop his screaming."

"Did you drive to the hospital or not?" Sarah asked.

"Yes, I threw on my clothes, locked the house and drove through the snowstorm. I parked the car and asked the nurse at the receptionist desk which floor I needed. When I got off the elevator, I approached the nurses' station and introduced myself. I thought she looked at me as though she couldn't put the two of us together.

"I wasn't sure what I was expected to do or where I got the courage, but I told the woman confidently that I thought I could calm him down. I asked them to show me where he was and they agreed to let me in the room, but told me they would lock it once I was inside to make sure that he couldn't get out. I was told that I could buzz for the nurse if I needed help."

"Weren't you scared?"

"I wasn't scared, Sarah, because I knew he was tied down and couldn't hurt me, but I walked in not knowing what I would see. I looked at Steve, battered with bruises around his face and head, spots of dried blood on his arms, hands and chest. Despite what he had done to me, my heart ached for his pain and the demon that had caused him to do what he had done. I talked to him calmly. I tried to offer comfort. He cried. He said over and over again how sorry he was. After thirty minutes or so, I told him I would untie one of his legs, which I did. Once I felt comfortable, after another thirty minutes went by, I untied his other leg. He had calmed down considerably and now, close to six o'clock, about an hour after I had arrived, I untied one hand. Another two hours later, I untied the other hand. He was calm and was no longer a threat.

"I called for the nurse and she came in with another woman who was dressed in a suit. The woman in the suit introduced herself and asked me to step outside the room. She told me that she had met with her staff and the doctors who diagnosed Steve as an alcoholic. She then told me they were admitting Steve to a rehabilitation center in a neighboring town where he would stay for twenty-eight days.

"I told her I didn't agree with their diagnosis because in five years I could count on one hand the number of times I had seen my husband drunk. I told her that he suffered from psychological problems, some from childhood, the death of his mother, and most recently from the death of his daughter. I told her, as emphatically as possible, that Steve didn't need a rehab center, he needed psychiatric help. The hospital didn't agree. They released him to my care for twenty-four hours until the next morning when I was supposed to drive him to the rehabilitation center.

"I was nervous. We arrived home mid-morning and I wasn't sure if I was safe in the house alone with Steve. I was worried that if Steve saw the condition of the house it might trigger a reaction, and wasn't sure if he would try to hurt me again. As soon as we walked in the door, the fumes of the paint and turpentine were overpowering. The kitchen was still a mess – pills and broken dishes on the counters and floors. There was no way Steve didn't know right away what he had done. When I took him to the bedroom to help him into bed, it was impossible to miss the walls splattered with paint which he must have thrown after discovering I had run from the house the night before.

"Steve began to cry again when he saw the destruction, begging for forgiveness. He slept through the day and well into the night which gave me a chance to clean up the mess in the kitchen. The next morning, I drove Steve to the rehab center hoping that the program could 'cure' him and life would go on. Deep down I was most relieved that he was going to be out of the house for twenty-eight days and I was safe.

"I was so scared not knowing what the future would be like. I didn't tell anyone because of my shame and embarrassment. I thought people would think less of me because of my mistake marrying him. I had always tried to present Steve to everyone as a wonderful man."

"I can see why you would feel that way, Caroline. But I hope you didn't blame yourself for what happened. So, we must have met for our first night of knitting right after this episode?" Beth clarified.

"Yes, I think it was within weeks after that night."

For the next week, Beth couldn't get Caroline's story out of her mind. She had been able to feel Caroline's pain in perhaps having made the wrong choice.

The next week, Beth revisited the conversation from the previous week.

"It's strange that you look back, Caroline, and said you began to question your decision to marry Steve. I look back at my decisions and wish sometimes I had a second chance. Even if I did, I ask myself, knowing then what I know now, what would I have done differently?"

Caroline asked Beth, "Have you ever regretted giving the baby up for adoption? What did you have to do?"

"Each August we vacationed in New Hampshire and I remember that on the twenty-fourth of August, my father told me that he and I would be traveling to Boston to sign the adoption papers with Catholic Family Services. The lies continued and my siblings were told that my father was taking me to view a possible college I would be attending in another year. We left early in the morning for another quiet ride. My father pressed me with questions as to whether or not I had any doubts about signing the papers and then went on to tell me what was expected of me. I would sign the papers, not ask questions, that would be the end of it and we would be back to the vacation home by supper. It was back to life as normal – again.

"We arrived in Boston after a near silent two-hour ride. I had nothing to say and what possible questions could I have? We were met by one of the administrators at the agency who fulfilled her legal obligations by explaining the process and what it meant. Her words were wasted on me as I couldn't digest or didn't want to digest anything she was saying. I was asked if I had any questions. What difference did it make? I had no choices. I shook my head no. I was again numb, going through the motions expected of me. A packet of legal looking documents was placed on the table in front of me and the woman indicated where I was to sign. There was a moment of confusion as the woman explained I must have been so disassociated while in the hospital that I had signed papers there with three different names; the alias I used in Illinois so no one could trace my real name, my birth given name and another name I didn't recognize. That necessitated the signing of multiple pieces of adoption papers in triplicate making sure all bases were covered in the records. I was told that all birth and adoption papers would be sealed and that no one would ever be able to trace my name or that of the baby. There was closure again. That part of my life was over. Or so I thought at the time.

"My father had raised the question with me during a phone call in April as to where I wanted to go to school the following year for my last year of high school. He asked did I want to return to the small private school they had sent me to, return to my high school or even go away to a private boarding school. I took a deep breath and for the first time was not going to allow a major decision such as this to be made by someone else. This was an important decision. I needed the support from my friends. I needed to be where I felt welcomed, safe, in a familiar setting. I needed to be back at my high school and told him that was what I wanted. He challenged my decision but I held fast despite what I could hear through the phone lines as his teeth tightened in disapproval. He tried to talk me out of it but I held fast. I actually clenched my jaw, too, and said affirmatively, 'No. I want to go back to my old school', and so it was that in September, I was back in my old high school."

"Good for you, Beth. You found your voice! It must have felt wonderful", Caroline said with her fist raised in the air. Sarah clapped in agreement.

"On the first day of school, we were placed alphabetically in our seats and as my last name and Jack's started with the same letter, we were often seated near each other; so close that I could barely breathe at times-so close physically, but eons away on the inside. Putting on a good front became my full-time job. I would not beg for his compassion, his understanding, his support. His actions had proven that his feelings for me were shallow and clearly in the past.

"What was more uncomfortable for me was when the teacher introduced a new student seated behind me who had moved to town from Illinois during the summer. How ironic that this student had transferred from the same school I was supposed to have attended in my imaginary life. My classmates never spoke of my six months away and although the reasons were never revealed, I knew they all knew the real story. No one ever spoke of it so there was no way that the new student would ever know that I was supposed to have been his classmate in Illinois. I continued to hold my head high."

"That's almost too hard to believe! What are the chances of that?" questioned Caroline incredulously.

"I spent my senior year holding myself together. My yearbook picture captured a young scowling woman lacking any softness in her expression. In later years, I was told repeatedly, even by strangers, that my smile was beautiful. No one would have believed it if they had seen my yearbook picture.

"I was still in 're-entry- mode at the start of the school year, trying to pull my mind emotionally out of the imaginary wonderfully happy life I had experienced in Illinois. I was struggling to cope with keeping the deep secret inside, balancing the friendship of classmates, trying to be a person who didn't have a care in the world while shriveling inside. I wore the worry in my eyes in that yearbook picture, the sadness, and the grief. I was truly grieving the loss of my baby, the loss of Jack whom I still loved, the loss of my childhood and even, the loss of my family.

"I think it was years later before that smile would return in earnest. I began to withdraw further and returned to the habit of spending hours again lying on my bed staring out the window at the limbs of the trees where I could identify shapes, figures, even faces of animals or people. My mother would occasionally open the bedroom door and with exasperation shout, 'Why do you shut yourself inside your room?' I never answered. I just looked at her speechless as she closed the door. To be fair, I know she was clueless as to how to react to me, treat me or help me. My room was my safe place, somewhere I could withdraw within myself without explanation or apologies. When not creating objects and faces in the limbs of the trees, I continued to knit and knit and knit.

"Our graduation was held outside on the football field on a beautiful summer night in late June. Again, because of our last names, Jack and I ended up walking beside each other in the processional. Our proximity had little to do with my intuitive awareness of where he was, as though my antennae picked up his closeness. It was a soul connection. During graduation day, we exchanged yearbooks and added a message beside our picture in our classmate's book. Jack's message was short and to the point; 'Dear Beth, I could do a lot of reminiscing about the times we've had but the space allowance prohibits it. I'll just say I'll always remember you as a great friend; the girl with the best personality in our class…and more. Love always, Jack'.

"'I had made it through my senior year and looked forward to going away to college. I would be out of the house and saw college as a new beginning – a chance to meet new friends, live in a welcoming environment and perhaps allow myself to forgive and heal. I think the first year was a surprise because I actually enjoyed the friends I made. No one knew anything about my background so I could leave the stigma I felt with my history behind. Because my roommate had the same first name as I, as did the girl across the hall, I volunteered to reduce the confusion and use my middle name which seemed to help my transformation into a new identity."

"What is your middle name?" Caroline wanted to know.

"It's Lynn. I went to some social events at college but didn't go out of my way to meet anyone or date. Some of the women in the dormitory asked why I never seemed to want to go to any of the places where men gathered, but I shrugged off their invites with an explanation that I had studying to do or was just too tired. My heart wasn't in it. I was a little afraid to feel anything. And then an envelope arrived."

"I bet I know what you're going to say! Let me guess. Was it from Jack?" ventured Sarah.

"Yes! On the Monday just before the start of the Christmas break, I walked to the administration building as I did every day to pick up my mail. I pulled an envelope from the box and stared at the address recognizing immediately the handwriting. There was no need to turn it over to see the return address. I was shaking and couldn't get back to the privacy of my dorm room fast enough.

"Jack's note was short but with feeling. He wrote that he thought of me often. There were pleasantries, 'How was I? He hoped I was enjoying college.' There was a newsy section about his first semester at school and what was happening in his life. He was enjoying college and looking forward to attending the Academy, finally beginning to realize his dream to become a pilot. Then he asked, 'Can I see you during the holiday break?' He said he would call me after we got home. He signed the letter, 'Love always, Jack'. I cried without knowing exactly what I was crying about. I wasn't sure if I was crying about the past or the future. I was so excited by the letter and shocked that he had wanted to see me. My mind started to go wild. I began to imagine that it meant he still cared or was he experiencing a twinge of guilt? He wanted to see me. 'Why?' I wondered."

"I hope you didn't set yourself up for more hurt. Why do you think he wanted to see you, Beth?"

"I wasn't sure. I know what I hoped was the reason.

"The day after Christmas, Jane called to tell me that Jack had called her to act as a mediator. I had, of course, told him that I wasn't supposed to see him or have any contact with him. Despite the fact that my parents didn't like Jane, they gave me permission to spend the night at her house. An hour before Jack was to pick me up at Jane's house, I felt as though I was suffocating. My heart was racing. I was hyperventilating.

"I watched as he got out of his car and walked to the front door. Jack walked in with open arms pulling me toward him with a warm hug. I allowed myself to open my arms and let him get close. I could feel his chest against mine and his back against the palms of my hands. He stepped back and smiled at me. I was melting inside but holding back so as not to let him see how much I still cared for him or the depth of my feelings."

"We went to the movies, a drive-in theater actually, which was still open despite the fact that it was December. It allowed us privacy, a place to talk, a spot to reconnect but I was afraid to show my feelings. I was being very cautious because I didn't want to be rejected and abandoned again. I knew no one could abandon me if it appeared that I didn't care or feel or express a need."

"Did you really go to a drive-in in December or are you just saying that?"

"No, we did. But you're not going to believe what movie was playing. It was called "A Summer Place" with Troy Donahue and Sandra Dee. The movie was a 1959 romantic drama filmed when Troy Donahue was a teen idol. The parallels of the relationship of the two main characters in the movie to the relationship Jack and I had had were uncanny. I had no idea what the film was about when Jack suggested it but I could have been its author, director and producer."

"Do you think Jack picked that movie on purpose? Do you think he knew what the movie was about?"

"I don't think so, Caroline, because there was only one drive-in and one movie playing, so there really wasn't a choice. We watched whatever was showing. It's just bizarre it was that movie.

"The story was about the adult lives of two onetime teenage lovers, Molly Jorgenson, played by Sandra Dee and Johnny Hunter played by Troy Donahue. Molly's parents disapproved of Johnny and had forbidden them to see each other, however, Molly becomes pregnant and asks her parents for their permission to marry. The movie centers on their lives as adults years later and Johnny's battle with alcoholism. Their story ends with Molly and Johnny happily married- an ending I would have wanted more than anything.

"I really couldn't believe what I was watching because it seemed that on a large cinema screen, Sandra Dee was acting out my life and there was my Johnny sitting next to me, his arm resting on my shoulder, his other hand holding mine. I felt at peace at last. I felt this was where I belonged. There was no turmoil. The movie was impassioned and I believe Jack sensed the correlation as I did, although neither one of us said, 'Wow, that's us'! Almost simultaneously something stirred within each of us. The electricity between the two of us was still there even with all that had happened in our past. We had been lovers and this was the man I never wanted to leave. I would have run to the corners of the world had he asked.

"When his hand moved down my arm, I turned and he leaned over and kissed me. He put his arms around me, pulled me into his chest which initially made me feel safe at last. This was where I should have been all along. He kissed me again, this time more passionately and I kissed him back. I wanted to stay in his embrace forever. He started to breathe more heavily.

"I felt his hand move under my blouse and was shocked. As much as I wanted him to care about me, I was speechless that after all that had happened between us, he thought it could take place again. I kept thinking this isn't really happening. I don't know why I did what I did because every bit of me wanted him and wanted to feel him close. I actually physically ached to be close to him but something nagged at me that I didn't want to be used and abandoned again. I forcefully pushed him away. He stopped and moved away. He looked at me lovingly and I stared back into his eyes. He seemed surprised that I had pushed him away and looked apologetic that he had misread my desires. He simply said, 'I will always love you; you know. You will always be a part of me no matter where you are. 'I felt tears fill my eyes. I couldn't speak the words I felt. I couldn't tell him that I wanted to be a part of his life forever, that being with him was 'home' to me. I was afraid of being left again. I've always wondered what would have happened if I had said what I thought."

"Do you think it would have made a difference to him, Beth? What do you think he had in mind when he said he wanted to see you? Do you think he just wanted to see you to have sex?"

"I don't think so, Caroline. He sounded as though he was sincere when he told me how he felt about me. I think he saw it as an expression of his feelings; at least that's what I wanted to think. But he just started the car and we drove back to Jane's house. Neither one of us mentioned anything about ever seeing each other again. He kissed me goodbye at Jane's door and told me again that he loved me, that I meant more to him than anyone he had ever known."

"Your heart must have been breaking."

"It was, Sarah. I quickly said goodbye first, feeling if I left first, I was not being abandoned again. It had been my choice to leave, but my heart was breaking."

"So that was the end, Beth? You never saw him again?"

"No, Caroline, I saw him. It was twenty-one years later and just a couple of years ago. It was strange the way it all came about and I ended up back with him."

"I went back to college, saddened that my evening with Jack had ended the way it had. I picked up my needles, knitting with a vengeance. I gave a sweater to everyone I knew. I was not interested in the end product, but just the process of preoccupation. During my third year at college, I met Ed who was a junior at a nearby men's university. I found him to be quite handsome and interesting. He was intelligent, tall, and a football player. The highlight of my junior year was attending his football games on Saturday afternoons where I sat in the stands feeling special to be 'Ed's girl'. More than once I wondered if there was a parallel to my previous life. I wasn't sure. It wasn't long before we fell madly in love and saw each other every weekend.

"As we became more serious, I felt compelled to be honest and share with Ed my history, not sure if I was seeking his approval or acceptance. I had lived a life of lies and deceit long enough. I wanted nothing less than to be completely honest. His reaction to my story was what mattered. He immediately reached out and engulfed me with a warm hug expressing his grief for my suffering and loss. We graduated the following year from our respective colleges and Ed was hired by a bank at a neighboring town. A few years after Ed and I married, I returned to a local college and earned credits toward a degree in teaching. Everything looked bright except that Ed and I had fallen so far apart, there was little left of our relationship. We seldom even talked."

"Did you ever try to speak to Ed about your concerns, Beth?"

"Sarah, I tried so many times. I even asked him to come into the living room one Sunday afternoon, pointed to the seat beside me on the couch and said, 'Let's talk'. I got a blank stare and the response, 'There's nothing worth talking about.'"

"I wanted so much to have an emotional connection, but Ed seemed caught up in his career and sports; both of us were consumed in our roles of trying to be good parents to our children while losing sight of what was happening to our marriage. We went through motions and, looking back, I accept responsibility for much of the distance.

"Even hearing the word 'pregnant' would start a huge panic attack. Sitting in my evening college class, one night, the professor mentioned the word 'reproduction' which sent me into instant perspiration. My face got hot and flushed and the heat was so extreme, I was sure everyone knew and saw my humiliation. I couldn't control the attacks because the harder I tried to stop them, the worse they became. I just had to try and survive them until they passed."

"What did you do while you were having them? Could you put your head down or pretend to cough or something like that so no one would notice?"

"Sarah, sometimes I prayed and forced myself to think of a happy thought. I tried anything to distract myself mentally. The attacks scared me and together with the nightmares I was having, I was exhausted. I used prayer to try and calm my inner fears and used knitting as a way to lessen some of the anxiety. I don't know how much worse it would be if I didn't have our group for support.

"I constantly wondered what was my baby's name? Did he have my hazel eyes or Jack's blue eyes? He had weighed ten pounds at birth and I wondered if he was a big boy still. I questioned where he might live and who were his parents? Was he a good baby? I looked at every baby about the same age and thought 'Could that baby be mine?' Whether I was on a bus, or walking down the sidewalk, the image of my baby never left me; I regretted that I had not walked down the hallway of the hospital to see my baby. At least I would have in my mind's eye a picture of my child as an infant, a point of reference. I had no such image in my mind to connect to.

"I think part of my panic was because, my own children were getting older and I would sometimes wake up with nightmares that someone had come knocking on my door. When I answered it, standing before me were the adoptive parents of my baby. I lived in daily fear that someday someone would knock on my door and announce he was my son. What would I tell my children? How could I explain this person? Would they think I was a horrible person? I went so far as to wonder if my children would still love me.

"We lived in a small town where Ed was seen as a fine Little League coach and I worried if my secret was discovered, would it being shame to him and my children? How could I live with more shame? I was in such mental turmoil but was afraid to share any of these fears with my husband. I began to pull away from him, my mind occupied with random fearful thoughts and turmoil. I felt my marriage slipping away but didn't know how to save it. On top of all the other guilt I felt, now I felt more because I knew I was hurting my husband.

"I stopped eating, existing on little food thinking perhaps if I purged my body, I could purge my mind and soul of all those scary emotions. Perhaps that would bring me peace, some comfort. I poured myself into trying to be the best student possible and the best mother I could be, always trying to be someone better. I began to lose weight and feel better about myself but was surviving on such small amounts of food. It seemed as though not even knitting could help me.

"I just became weaker and weaker. I returned to school after the summer to finish my last year and earn my degree. Two weeks into the semester, with four young children at home, I arrived home and didn't have the strength or energy to walk the ten-foot hallway to even answer a phone. I was unable to move. I had never felt so tired – so lifeless. I had no idea what the problem was but knew intuitively that there was something wrong with me.

"Two days later, the doctor diagnosed me with acute hepatitis and ordered me to check into the hospital. I refused and replied that with four young children I could not be admitted to a hospital. I assured him that I would get a nurse to help me which we did. I found a fellow student who would be 'my legs' between classes so I would not have to withdraw from school. I was bedridden for five months. The jaundice had turned my eyes yellow and I was told my liver was in serious condition. The doctor warmed that one side effect of the disease was severe depression."

"That must have been a very rough period of time for you, Beth," Sarah said in a sympathetic tone.

"It was, but the depression from the disease actually intensified the anxiety and insomnia. I was so bone tired I had to be dependent on the nurse and Ed, and you know how I feel about being dependent on anyone." Beth offered.

"Although I had been warned about depression and anticipated it, I had no idea of the depth of despair. I found myself lying in bed crying uncontrollably – unable to explain what I was crying about. The doctor ordered a sedative and anti-depressant which I reluctantly took. I never used drugs as I didn't like how they made me feel. After all, how could I depend on myself if I wasn't able to be in full control of my thoughts and actions? I couldn't risk jeopardizing my inner strength. I couldn't count on myself if I was in any kind of weakened state. I had to be strong."

As soon as I was able to sit up, I continued to knit frantically in bed and use knitting to relieve stress and take my mind off the turmoil inside.

"So, you finished the school year?" Sarah wondered.

"Oh yes. I finished three years and was excited to be offered an elementary teaching position in the fall." Beth explained.

"I became better physically but mentally the disease had weakened my emotional state further. Out of desperation when I thought I would no longer be able to get through each day, I started seeing a therapist."

Beth began to feel she was monopolizing the conversation.

"Sarah, how did your meeting go with Rick?"

The women were anxious to hear about Sarah's meeting with Rick.

"During the morning hours, I worked for a writer in town typing his boy's mystery novel, which kept me entertained for at least part of the day then during the afternoons I hung out with friends at the community pool. Rick, the lifeguard, approached me one afternoon as I was sitting knitting and talking to a bunch of my friends. He sat down and asked me if I wanted to go with him to the refreshment stand for a Coke. Halfway through our drink, he asked me to go to the movies the following Saturday night."

"On Saturday, I was sitting in the backyard with my father when Rick arrived to pick me up. I remember him walking confidently toward my father with an outstretched hand. He shook my father's hand, introduced himself and I think impressed my father with his manners and confidence. He looked nice. He had on gray slacks, a white oxford shirt and a sharp madras jacket. It was a nice night and it felt good to be going out again on a date after such a long time. At the end of the night, Rick promised to call and said he'd see me the next day at the pool.

"The next day, Rick walked over and said he had a good time and seeing me knitting, asked jokingly, 'Hey can you make me a sweater for my birthday?' I smiled and said with a giggle, 'Of course', and Rick added, 'My birthday's in two days.' I just very calmly said, 'No problem' and kept knitting. Two days later on Rick's birthday, I rang the doorbell and handed Rick's brother a gift-wrapped package for Rick."

"You actually knit Rick a sweater in two days?" Beth asked incredulously.

"Yup, I did. But the sweater was a miniature size measuring only five inches by five inches."

"What a hoot!" Beth chuckled. "What was his reaction?"

"He had a good sense of humor and told me that night he thought it was very clever of me.

"We dated the rest of the summer and then went off to college in the fall. We wrote almost every day and called each other a lot. When we were home for college breaks, we saw each other every day. Rick was a year ahead of me in school and when he graduated, I was very proud of him. I liked Rick's family a lot and they seemed to like me as well.

"Right after graduation, Rick took a job with a high-tech company and I found a summer job working at the local movie theater at night selling tickets. On August twelfth, Rick walked up to the ticket book, leaned over as though he was going to purchase a ticket and said, 'If you will marry me, I will take care of you for the rest of your life.'"

"That's sweet. Were you surprised?"

"I was, but I immediately said 'YES', and stepped out of the booth long enough to give him a hug. He suggested that we celebrate on the weekend and we agreed to be engaged for the year while I finished school and to marry the following summer.

"I completed my college education and graduated with a degree in English. Everything looked bright. Life was good. We had a beautiful wedding at Rick's parents' lakeside summer home followed by a sit-down dinner and band in their side yard.

"From the start, Rick was true to his word. He treated me with such love and care I wondered what I had done to be so fortunate. I was continually pampered. There was nothing I lacked. We bought a beautiful home which I decorated with love; Rick admired every final touch I added to each room. He insisted I stay at home and work as a homemaker and assured me I would be taken care of; he thought his role in life was to provide for me and hopefully our future family."

"Sarah, he sounds too good to be true! Lucky you," Caroline remarked.

"Rick had been raised by loving parents in a family with three sisters and was taught good manners by his father from an early age. His father taught him to open the door for his sisters, and pull the chair out when they were to sit at the table - all lessons designed to make a gentleman out of a young boy. Perhaps that was the explanation as to why Rick felt a compelling need to be a caregiver. As I've said before, I think I felt loved for the first time and it felt really good.

"Before Rick leaves for work, we sit together and talk over coffee. He asks me each morning, as he rubs lotion on my back after my shower, what my day looks like. When he's at work, he calls me a few times a day to ask what I was doing, explaining that he missed me and liked to picture what I was doing at home during my day."

"It sounds very romantic. I can't imagine a man who likes to talk like that and pays so much attention to me! You're a lucky girl." Beth said.

Caroline added, "He's a keeper!"

"There's more. At night while I read and Rick watches television, I get a foot rub for hours! He's the most thoughtful caring person I had ever met. He finds the littlest things to do to show me he loves me. He even takes my car and fills the tank because he knows the smell of gasoline makes me feel sick.

"When he mows the lawn on weekends, he checks with me when he's done to see if it passes my inspection! I can't believe how much he does for me."

"Wow, there are a lot of wives who would be thrilled to be treated that way, Sarah".

Over the next weeks, Caroline and Beth helped Sarah move into her house. The holidays were celebrated with family and the ladies returned to the loft to begin a new year of companionship, toasting their friendship with a glass of Chablis.

After an exchange of holiday family stories, Caroline was anxious to get the support of Sarah and Beth about a nagging question in her mind.

"I keep wondering if I could have done something differently that would have prevented Steve from going out of control that night. I don't think I blamed myself because I still think Steve needs some counseling and I'm hoping the rehab center deals with the psychological part of his problems. The day after I took him to the center, I knew I needed something to help me with my stress. The new yarn shop at just opened in town. I walked in thinking it would be the answer I needed."

"What's it like at the rehab center, Caroline?" Sarah asked.

"There's always a meeting while I'm there that I go to. It doesn't look like a hospital. There's a big cafeteria and different small meeting rooms. I have to confess something though."

"Go ahead, Caroline. What are you thinking?" Beth urged.

"I am livid! I mean really livid", Caroline hissed.

"There is an attitude on Steve's part that he's on a holiday! He laughs with everyone and they all joke about this liquid they drink they all call 'the green juice'. It's supposed to lessen their withdrawals but Steve acts like he's on a drug-induced high. It infuriates me!"

"Have you figured out what makes you so angry?"

"Sarah, why am I the only one who seems to be suffering? Why is it that Steve is acting like he's at a party and he's the center of attention! I'm scared, angry and suffering and he is having a great time! That's what infuriates me!"

"When you called, Beth, I had just taken him to the center and it was the thought of the knitting group and a

Wednesday night out that was my salvation. The fact that Steve was in the center meant I didn't have to worry about being out one night a week although I knew he would be angry that I wouldn't be visiting him on Wednesday night. I didn't care. I needed to do something for me."

"There are groups for friends and families of alcoholics, Caroline. I think it's called Al-Anon. Have you thought about joining?" Beth asked.

"Yes, they have the Al-Anon meetings at the center so I've been to a few. I'm trying to do my part to be constructive and help to understand so maybe I can help Steve and make my life better, too. I've been reading and finding some peace and, I admit, hope. I've already learned I'm a classic enabler because I keep the trauma of my marriage a secret to protect Steve and hide my embarrassment. By keeping quiet, I've allowed him to continue his behavior and control me with his anger. I've learned when you are married to an alcoholic, the tendency is to enable unacceptable and abusive behavior; look the other way. I was embarrassed, Sarah. I want my family and friends to like my husband. I feel his behavior is a reflection on me; the terrible choice I had made. I don't want anyone to see the 'real' Steve. I've been enabling him to protect my reputation and appearance."

"I get it, Caroline," Sarah acknowledged. "I think in a way I have been an enabler too with my husband, Rick, but not because he's an alcoholic. I've given the signal that I like how he acts, at least I did at one time. Now it's bothering me and I'm really struggling. But it's late. It can wait until next week."

"Sarah, what if you tried to gently speak to Rick this week and explain you want to try and figure some things out for yourself. Even if you don't like the smell of gas, try filling your own tank?" Beth suggested.

The flu hit both Caroline and Sarah so for three weeks the women were unable to meet. It seemed like forever to each of them. When they resumed their group, Beth could hardly wait until Sarah and Caroline were in their seats.

"A week ago, I had the weirdest thing happen in therapy. I've told you about my therapist whom I've been seeing every week for the past three years. I sit in a comfortable chair and pour out my heart and soul to this man that I think of as my lifeline. The first few sessions I talked about typical things like my childhood, my parents, my upbringing."

"Was it hard, Beth?" Sarah asked.

"Not at the beginning because my sessions felt as though I was just giving a report. It didn't get difficult until months later when I had to talk about the most painful things. Sometimes I spoke with anger and sometimes I had trouble speaking at all because I was crying so hard. When we got closer to talking about my loneliness and abandonment issues, I cried a lot. But I began to notice a different feeling inside my chest after about a year or so."

"Why kind of feeling?" Sarah asked.

"It's strange but I began to almost feel a lightening in my chest, my heart. The more I talked and the deeper I got into all that I had stuffed inside me, the lighter my chest felt. I felt my heart starting to open up a little. Each week it got a little easier."

"Do you think it was just the talking to him that did it or do you think it was something more?"

"My therapist has been really pushing me to see things from a different perspective. He's shown me how to look at why I felt the way I did and what caused those feelings.

I've been able to let go of some of the shame and guilt and see that some of it wasn't my fault. And he taught me a lifesaving exercise for panic attacks."

"I sometimes have anxiety attacks, so I would love to know what he taught you." Caroline admitted.

"It works! I've been using the technique for almost three years and I've not had another panic attack. He told me when I feel the anxiety starting, stop and don't run from it mentally. That makes it worse. He told me to stop and search my brain for what was happening at the moment the attack started. He urged me not to be frightened, but to think, was something said that caused the attack to start? Had I seen something? What was I thinking at the time it began? He said, 'Pretend you are an innocent observer. Maybe you're looking through a window or you're up in the sky'. At first, it was difficult. But once I mastered it and was able to figure out what the cause of the attack, they stopped."

Caroline was excited. "That's fantastic! I'm going to try it."

"Yeah, basically I took control of my attacks. They weren't controlling me. Sometimes I even say under my breath, 'Come and get me!' and now I'm free from them entirely."

"For all the years I've been going and talking about everything from my childhood to my teenage pregnancy, I've, of course, never mentioned Jack's name. There just was never any reason to. I'm still in shock after my session yesterday."

Sarah and Caroline had stopped knitting.

"By mistake yesterday, in the course of conversation, I mentioned Jack's name and how I wished I could see him and bring closure to that part of my life. I was explaining that I thought the therapy had helped me with the pain of my parents and childhood, but the whole issues with Jack were unsettling. I looked over at my therapist who was sitting and staring at me, his jaw open and speechless – obviously I said something startling."

"What was it? What had you said?"

"Sarah, that's the point. I hadn't said anything to get the reaction I got from the therapist.

"My therapist said he thought it was important for my mental health to bring closure to my relationship with Jack and that without it, I would be frozen in time and unable to move forward since Jack and my pregnancy had had such a huge impact on my life and was continuing to affect it."

"What did you think about what he suggested? Was that something you wanted to do?" Caroline asked.

"I want to get healthy. I want to put all the pain to rest. I want to forgive myself. I want to forgive Jack. So yes, I would want to see him. Just saying that though makes me hyperventilate. My therapist then told me that it would be important for Jack, as well as, he was sure Jack was carrying feelings about the same issue and would want to move on."

"There's more isn't there?" Sarah suggested.

"Yes. He said he had been counseling a young man who suffered tremendous guilt and remorse stemming from a pregnancy when he was a teenager. He talked about how much he loved this girl and had abandoned her. He had been struggling for years looking for forgiveness and being pain free."

"Oh my gosh, Beth! Should he have told you that? Wasn't he being unethical?"

"I thought that at first, Sarah, but I think he knew it was something that would heal both of us and allow each of us to move forward and put the past behind us. I think he knew it was in our best interest to help us both. He had just never connected the pieces over the years of working with both of us in two different offices."

Sarah immediately hopped on Beth's latest revelation. "Your therapist must have been shocked! No wonder he wasn't able to put all the pieces together from each of you if he was seeing each of you in two different offices, an hour apart. I'm not a big believer in fate or God's will but it seems to me this is a little bit out of the norm. Don't you think, Caroline?"

"It does seem uncanny. I agree. So, are you going to do it?"

"I told the therapist I would meet Jack if he was agreeable to it. Our therapist said he would see Jack next week and suggest it. He would let me know next week when I see him."

"I don't know how I'll get through the week waiting to find out what he comes back with."

"You? I'm a little frightened. I have no idea what to expect if I came face to face with the man that I've carried with me for so many years. I've tried so hard to let him go and leave the past in the past. I guess I'm afraid for me and my children. I just don't know where this is all going and it's scary."

"Speaking of scary, I want to tell you what happened at dinner with Steve the other night. I picked him up at the rehab center the day before yesterday. I can't believe the twenty-eight days went by so fast. I've just had this nagging feeling that the hospital's diagnosis was wrong. I thought so then and I think so now but no one will believe me"

"Why has something happened, Caroline?" both women asked also simultaneously.

"No, not really. It's just very strange. Steve shows no signs that he misses alcohol, answers the calls from his sponsor, and listening to him you would never think anything happened. He was supposed to go to an AA meeting last night but at the last minute, decided not to. He just is no different than he was before he stopped drinking."

"What happened when you got home? Did he seem glad to be there?"

"Sarah, he walked in the door as though he had just been shopping for groceries, and announced he was going to unpack and said he needed a nap. I couldn't wait to escape and go upstairs to my desk and pretend things were back to normal-whatever that was. I just couldn't wait to escape and come here. I have really felt in the past few days, I needed a soft place to land."

"Are you frightened at all that he might do something again?" Beth asked, then suggested, "You can always come stay at my house if you feel in danger."

"We move through the day, eat dinner and then at night watch tv. The first night when we went to bed, I hugged the edge. I was afraid to touch Steve and did not sleep well at all. I kept waiting for something to happen during the night. In the back of my mind, I wondered if I was sharing the bed with a potential murderer and then decided my imagination was running away with me."

"I think what you're feeling is normal and it's going to take some time for you to feel safe again and assured that he's not going to have a relapse."

"I think you're right, Beth. Yesterday, Steve answered calls from his AA sponsor assuring him again that everything was fine. Steve mentioned for the third time that he wants to invite this young man, probably in his early twenties, for dinner. Steve seems to have latched on to him and seems intent on mentoring this kid while Steve is in recovery. I just keep wondering how he can help someone else when I'm not convinced, he can help himself."

"Maybe that's what he needs, Caroline" Beth suggested. "Maybe it will give him a reason to heal himself so he can help this kid heal."

"Caroline, have you been to any more Al-Anon meetings?"

"I've been to a few but I'm reading a lot about alcoholism and, without a doubt, I have been enabling Steve."

"I'm beginning to think I've been enabling and encouraging Rick to treat me the way he does – all the things he does for me from foot rubs, to filling my gas tank, calling me three or four times during the day. I'm having trouble with all of it now."

"What do mean you're having trouble with it? He's not doing it anymore?" Beth asked.

"Last night, we were going out to dinner and I mentioned I had a headache. Before I could get up, Rick went and got two aspirins and a glass of water and handed them to me. Then we went to dinner and before I could take a piece of bread, Rick reached across and took a piece of bread, buttered it and put it on my plate."

"What's wrong with that, Sarah?"

"I was ready to scream, Beth. I wanted to yell for him to back off and give me some space. It was all too much."

"Wow, there are a lot of wives who would be thrilled to be treated that way, Sarah".

"At first, I did like it, Caroline, because it made me feel very loved but over the years things changed. I've changed. I'm not the young girl who needed to be taken care of. With Rick doing everything I had a lot of free time – too much, especially since, as you know, I always get up early in the morning and like to have my housework finished by mid- morning; which left many hours on my hands. Even though I love to read, it wasn't enough, so that's how I got back into knitting."

"Rick is happy that I had found new friends and enjoys Thursday morning over coffee to hear about the women and how our Wednesday night went. He always takes an interest in each story you would think he knew you. I keep asking myself what's wrong? I've been taken care of since I was twenty years old. It felt good. It felt as though I was loved. Every need I've had, Rick has met. I've not had to do a thing. I could buy whatever I wanted; go wherever I wanted to go."

"So, what's the difference now, Sarah?" Caroline asked.

"I've enabled him to treat me that way. I've allowed him to do so much for me that it feels like I've lost myself in our marriage. Sometimes I think where is 'me'? Who am I?"

Beth quickly confessed, "I can see exactly how you felt that way, Sarah. I think it goes back to what we talked about ages ago. How we either marry our fathers or seek a partner who we think gives us what our father didn't. I think Rick would hate being married to me because I'm too independent. It would make him miserable not to be needed."

"I know I've been the envy of the group and have been told often that my marriage was the best anyone had ever heard about. Time has passed and now I want some independence."

"I can understand why you would feel that way, Sarah."

"I always liked the fact that there was no need for me to do anything for myself. You've listened to me for Wednesday after Wednesday talk about what Rick surprised me with the week before, or something thoughtful that had happened during the week. Now after all these years, I don't know how to change it. I've not worked a day of my life since the summer I sold tickets at the movie theater."

"What do you want to do about it, Sarah?"

"I'm not sure. I'm hoping we can talk about it here. Beth, I know once you asked me years ago how I could stand not having my own money, feeling independent and capable of taking care of myself. I remember then I always shrugged my shoulders, perfectly content. I also remember that you thought you would find Rick smothering. I think you even went so far as to say you would feel he had violated your space. I didn't think any of those things back then. I couldn't understand what you were saying and have to admit, I thought you might have felt that way because you were jealous of me and how Rick treated me. Sorry for thinking that of you!

"Now I listen on Wednesday nights to both of you share your journey often including accomplishments, obviously and rightly so, I know you feel a sense of pride. Granted, I have raised two successful children and have kept a home which I'm proud of and Rick loves but I have few personal accomplishments to share. Now, if Beth asked me again the same questions about having my own money, having a sense of accomplishment for having earned it, my answers would be different. I'm beginning to feel a need to prove to myself that I'm a capable woman."

Caroline threw out a suggestion to Sarah. "I've been listening to how you've described Rick since we first met and have wondered why Rick feels compelled to take his caregiving role to such an extreme. Do you think he perhaps thrives on control? If that's the case, how are you going to separate loving gestures from his heart from his need to be in control?"

"That's an interesting idea, Caroline. I never considered the control factor, but have even wondered if Rick only felt loved if he is needed. Is he confusing a need to feel needed with a need to feel loved? Our whole relationship is morphing into something very different than how it's always been and that's scary."

"I think you better be prepared, Sarah, that Rick is going to be hurt and confused. If you can figure out what motivates him to act the way he does, then maybe you could find a way to convince him how important it is for you to meet some of your own needs without compromising his." Beth suggested.

"I've been kept willingly under a large umbrella for my entire marriage," Sarah acknowledged. "I used to like that life, but now I'm anxious and a little frightened to get out from under it and rely on me. I'm a little afraid of taking the first steps. I think that undoing the pattern my life has taken, is going to be very difficult and that's scary. More than once I've thought that maybe it's safer and easier to leave things the way they are, but my anger is going to get in the way. I know I should continue to feel loved and cherished by Rick's attention and acts of kindness, but I don't. I'm feeling, as Beth once said, smothered. My personal space is invaded every day. I am no longer the young bride looking for someone to take care of her."

For the next few weeks, the women continued to meet, anxious to hear how Sarah was coping with her fight for independence, and the outcome of Beth's meeting with Jack.

"I can't wait any longer, Beth. I know your meeting with Jack was two days ago. I've been on pins and needles! It was all I could do to keep from calling. What happened when you met Jack?"

"Our therapist arranged a neutral spot for our meeting halfway between our homes. We agreed to meet at a restaurant at noon and have lunch. I walked in and told the hostess I was meeting someone. With a questioning look on her face she pointed to a man sitting in the corner booth at the back of the room. I saw him immediately, even before she pointed to him."

"Were you dying?" Sarah wanted to know.

"I walked across the room trying to breathe normally and not appear too anxious. He stood up and, as soon as I reached his table, he opened his arms up and gave me a huge welcoming hug."

"Did you start to talk right away?"

"Caroline, I was so nervous. We hadn't seen each other in years and it took a while to get each of us caught up on careers, marriage, children – you know all those things you talk about and ask about when you meet someone new."

"But you weren't 'new'."

"I know, but we were strangers in a way. We had never met as adults. I ordered a salad but couldn't eat it. I just picked. I just knew that I was overcome with a feeling of peace and contentment. This was where I belonged."

"Did Jack seem to be nervous?" Caroline wanted to know.

"I don't think so. We talked about being in college, we talked about our careers and our families. Jack said he had been divorced a number of years and his former wife lived out west with their two children whom he saw only during the summer; something he shared with a lot of sadness in his voice. I didn't feel comfortable saying anything about the problems Ed and I are having."

"How long did you stay there?" Sarah asked.

"We were both so engrossed in conversation, that at some point we both looked out the window and discovered it was dark! We had spent the entire afternoon in a restaurant talking endlessly but never brought up the subject we were supposed to be talking about. I knew my therapist was right, but I didn't know how to open the conversation and say what I had wanted to say for over twenty years. I didn't want to ruin the day."

"So that was it?" Sarah asked. "That was the end?"

"No, we both agreed we would like to meet again and set a date to meet at Jack's house. He shared that he lived in an old house along the river and suggested perhaps I would like to stop by and we could sit in the garden and talk."

"Are you going?" Caroline asked.

"Absolutely! But Jack's schedule is full for the next few weeks, so it won't be until next month. It's going to seem like forever!"

Beth and Sarah were concerned about Caroline a few weeks later, knowing Steve had been home from the rehab center for almost a month. Beth asked, "Is everything alright with you and Steve? It's been almost a month now. Do you see any difference?"

"We get through each day. He finds things to do and I have to work of course, but it's definitely different. The other night, I couldn't stand the suspense any longer. I made us a nice dinner, actually Steve's favorite. As we were finishing, I took a deep breath, looked him in the eye and asked, 'That night, when I walked down the cellar stairs and you came after me with the ax, do you think you would have killed me?' I held my breath waiting for his answer. I was afraid what he would say."

"What did he say, Caroline? Did he seem angry that you asked?" Sarah wondered.

"No, he didn't seem angry. I just didn't know if I could believe his answer. He paused quite a while before answering me and then just said, 'No. I don't think so.' I didn't feel totally convinced. I'm trying to be positive and trusting. It's just hard sometimes."

"Things are going really well at work, which helps. I love my job as a sales rep and know I made the right decision. As much as I loved teaching, I enjoy working with adults. Something exciting happened yesterday. I was called into my manager's office and he asked if I would be interested in a promotion to a national position!"

"Congratulations! That's exciting Caroline. Are you going to take it?"

"I'm not sure, Sarah. I like the idea, but the downside is I'll be traveling a lot. You know what happens with Steve when I'm not around. I know I've got to do what I want. I told my manager I'd get back to him."

When Caroline announced a month later that she had decided to take the national sales position, Beth and Sarah shared in her excitement, but hesitantly asked, "What did Steve say?"

"I was surprised. He didn't seem to care one way or another, which is sort of what I mean when I say it's strange. He was matter of fact about it, actually. I think his mentoring that young man has given him a purpose and focus, so I don't think he's as dependent on me for security. He did surprise me the other day though. He wants to sell his boat. I doubt we'll ever sail again."

"How do you feel about that?"

"Are you kidding, Sarah! I'm thrilled. I was getting tired of sailing every weekend; there was never time for anything else. The other bit of news I have is, he wants to sell the house and move to a cabin on a lake near his sister who owns a cottage there."

"Gee, that's a major change! Do you want to sell?"

"You know, Beth, it might be just what we need. A change and new beginning; living in a house where there aren't the tragic memories we have now whenever we go room to room. I think it might be good for us. It's not that far and I can still get to our Wednesday nights, which is a very important consideration in the decision to move. Steve understands that. Okay, enough about me! I want to hear what happened when you went to Jack's house yesterday, Beth."

"You can imagine how nervous I was! I drove down the road that followed the river and knew, from Jack's description at the restaurant, exactly which house was his. It was really big and old. What a spot! It was painted a deep mustard color and had a dirt driveway from the road that wound around to the back of the house. His house is right on the river, a stone's throw. The only thing separating the front door and the river, is the road. His property is wooded in the back and on the sides with a lot of privacy because there weren't any nearby neighbors that I could see."

"It sounds incredible, Beth," Caroline said. "I'm hoping my new cabin on the lake turns out to be feel as peaceful as what you're describing Jack's house is like."

"I don't know if it was the location, the river or just being there, but I felt such peace and comfort in my heart. It was as though I was home. Jack came out as soon as I opened the car door and again greeted me with a warm hug. It seems a little awkward again and our words seems a little strained at first. He invited me into the house, and I had to hold my breath to keep from gasping. It was spectacular!"

"What was it like inside?" Sarah asked.

"It was filled with antique pieces of furniture and there were little groupings of collections like early candlesticks. There were a lot of pictures scattered throughout the living room; many of his children, which he described. Jack had made dinner which was quite good. We sat in the kitchen at the table and talked but again, neither one of us opened the conversation. When we finished dessert, we talked a little more; Jack about his job and I a little about our knitting group. He asked if we could meet again in a few weeks. Of course, I agreed and, after a hug, I left."

"What did you feel like the whole time you were sitting there, Beth?" Caroline asked.

"I was happy. I wanted to stay and enjoy the feeling of 'home at last', but I wanted to cry too. I know that sounds weird, but I wanted to cry because it hurt so much to be sitting there, across the table from Jack, in his home, but not part of his life. It was as though I was living my dream I had had for so many years, but this time I stayed instead of leaving the room with my husband."

The three women were each anxious to share all the events of the past month when they met the next Wednesday.

"I've got some good news!" Caroline announced. "Our house sold and we've moving this summer. One of Steve's friends bought the sailboat but we're keeping the dinghy to use on the lake so I think Steve feels he's taking a bit of his past with us to our new house."

"That's great news, Caroline. I think it's a good thing that you're moving. There's nothing like a fresh start and it sounds like Steve is doing alright."

"I think he is but he's stopped going to meetings and I don't think he tells his sponsor. I'm not sure what that means for the future. He seems a little distant and I notice again that his eyes dart to the side often when we are talking. That concerns me a little, but there haven't been any problems. He likes to go out and meet his young man he befriended from the center, so I have a little breathing room when he's gone."

"Talking about breathing room, Sarah, what's happening with you and Rick? Is he giving you any breathing room or are you still feeling smothered?" Caroline asked.

"Well, every morning, when we are sitting with our coffee before Rick leaves for work, I'm slowly trying to hint about things I've been doing on my own. Like, the other day he said he was going to take care of my car registration renewal, and I calmly told him, I'd taken care of it."

"What was his reaction?" Beth asked.

"He looked shocked. I think he was sitting there wondering how I could possibly know how to do that but he didn't say anything."

"Then last night we were watching television and Rick suddenly stood up and said he'd be right back. He was going to go fill my gas tank. I was a little nervous, so I just casually mentioned, 'Oh, I filled it yesterday'. Again, he didn't say anything but, I could tell he seemed a little put out."

"It sounds as though he's feeling a little displaced with what you're doing," Sarah commented.

"I think you're right because he put his coffee cup down on the table, looked at me and said, 'I've always taken care of you without asking for anything in return. You seem not to need me anymore. I'll just take care of myself', and he went off to get ready to go to work."

"Give him some time, Sarah. It's a big change for both of you and it's going to take some time to get used to your new roles. He's probably interpreting your actions as rejection. I bet he'll come around in a few weeks and realize that it doesn't mean you don't love him," Caroline suggested.

A month later, spring was in the air. The weather had warmed and the women were all active opening up their gardens. After sharing the best places to buy plants and sharing a few complaints about the difficulty of knitting with blistered hands from weeding, Sarah asked Beth to share what had happened when she went to Jack's house for the second time.

"I went last Monday. It was a beautiful afternoon and after Jack met me again in the driveway with a nice hug – he gives great hugs, by the way! He asked me if I wanted to go for a walk as he pointed to the woods behind his house. I was dressed in a suit since I'd just come from work, and as I looked down at my outfit including heels, he caught my message and invited me into the house to give me something else to wear. Again, I was struck by how I felt sitting in his kitchen waiting for him to bring me something.

"He came out with a yellow sweater and a pair of boots I suspect belonged to one of his kids, because they were too small for Jack and looked like something a kid would wear. I went into the bathroom and changed into this sweater which was way too big for me, but the boots fit. Jack was waiting for me in the kitchen and when I came back, he smiled and said I looked cute. I felt like crying."

"It sounds as though he meant it, Beth. What a sweet thing to say," Sarah commented.

"We walked along the river and then climbed to an open spot on top of a small hill. Jack suggested we sit where we could talk and look at the river below. He started the conversation by asking me if I had any interest in trying to find our child. Wow! I didn't know what to say. It kind of came out of nowhere and took me by surprise. I said 'Yes I would' but confessed I was afraid of how that would impact my life. Jack said he had the same concerns."

"Did he say anything more?" Caroline wanted to know.

"Yes, and this surprised me too. Jack told me how years ago, he had tried to find our child. That shocked me! He said he wanted to accept responsibility for his action and do what he could to make it right. He told me he had decided to write a letter to my father who he thought would know where our child was."

"Oh my gosh, Beth. Were you dying when you heard that? Just knowing what you've told us about your father, I can't imagine what your father did when he got that letter."

"Wait till you hear, Sarah. Jack wrote the letter, a very formal letter he said, and drove it to the post office because he doesn't have a mailbox at the house. Two days after mailing the letter, Jack received a phone call from the postmaster saying a letter had been found on the post office floor with Jack's return address."

"This is so bizarre, Beth." Sarah said.

"Jack said he drove to the post office to pick up the letter. He is such a firm believer in chance and coincidence, Jack interpreted the finding of the letter as a signal he should not have written it in the first place."

"What happened to the letter?"

"Can you believe it, Caroline? He said he tore the letter up and decided not to try and contact my father again. Jack ended the conversation by suggesting we should agree to contact each other if either one of us learned any information or was ever contacted by our child. I agreed."

"We talked for a while, then Jack suggested we sit out back in his garden which he was anxious to show me and obviously very proud of. The garden was patterned after the ones he had seen in Viet Nam during the war. It was beautiful and serene. The garden seemed to speak volumes of Jack's connection to nature and his commitment to create a place where he could find peace and calm. He shared that he had discovered in Viet Nam that the gardens there drew him in and it was where he went when he needed to meditate. He said when he returned from the war and bought the house, this garden was one of the first projects he took on."

"What did the garden look like, Beth?" Sarah asked, trying to picture it in her mind.

"It had trimmed shrubs and some statues similar to what you would expect to see in an Asian garden. There was a small pond with a fountain and some koi. He had even added a small bridge over one area.

"We sat down and Jack opened the conversation. I held my breath and knew what was coming. He started by first reminding me of how he had planned to attend the Academy in Colorado on his path to become a pilot. I nodded in acknowledgement. He paused and added, 'The Academy didn't permit married men to attend'. He paused I think to allow me time to absorb the meaning of what he had just said. I didn't say anything. I just looked at him. Then he said, 'I am so very sorry. Beth. Can you ever find it in your heart to forgive me?'"

Sarah and Caroline had both leaned forward in their seats, their needles on their laps, anxious to hear more.

"What did you say? Did his apology mean anything? Is that what you wanted to hear, Beth?" Caroline asked.

"I knew I had to follow the direction of my therapist if I hoped to heal, but the words were lost to me for a few minutes. When I finally found my voice, I asked him the question I'd had in my mind for years. 'Jack, all these years,

I've never even known where you ran away to. I had no idea where you were or even if you were safe.' I fought to hold back tears because I didn't want to lose the chance to finish this conversation."

"Did he tell you where he had gone?" Sarah said.

"He said, 'I hitchhiked to Florida and was picked up by truckers along the way. When I got to Florida, I found work in the fields and no one questioned me about who I was or where I came from.' He never told me where he stayed at night or how the police found him. I didn't ask. Then I started to cry, the pain written on my face, 'Do you have any idea what it felt like to be abandoned?' I didn't care right then if I was hurting his feelings. My anger was boiling up, consuming me and I couldn't control it. All the years of holding it in came rushing up."

"Did he try and stop you or make excuses to defend himself?" both women asked at the same time.

"No. He didn't try to make excuses for his behavior or try and stop me. He told me that he was terrified the night I had told him I thought I might be pregnant and saw all hope for his future disappear in a split second. He said everything he was doing in high school, the Student Council, the class president, the football star, were all part of the plan to become an airline pilot.

"His head was bent down in his hands, his fingers in his hair. I could see his shoulders shaking and I knew he was crying. He went on, 'I was so selfish. I saw how serious our relationship was and I didn't know how to manage it and still go to the Academy. I knew our relationship was leading to something serious and knew I might have to make a choice between us and the Academy. When you said you thought you might be pregnant, I saw my career path as impossible; my choice had been made."

"I don't understand something, Beth. Even if he was serious about you, it didn't mean you couldn't have waited until he finished at the Academy to get married. I agree your being pregnant created another problem, but he obviously felt he had to make a choice right then and saw no way to have both," Sarah concluded.

Beth nodded in agreement. "He said, 'I was scared and was a coward. I left a note on my bed for my mother so she wouldn't worry about me. I knew she would contact you but that's no excuse. I've always been disgusted with my behavior.' As he spoke, he began to sob harder. 'I've been in such pain all these years knowing the hurt I caused others, most of all you.'

"How did hearing that make you feel, Beth?" Sarah asked hoping that Jack's apology would give Beth some peace of mind.

"Seeing Jack in such pain was hard for me. He said after five months, the police found him and he was returned home. Then he added, 'I was glad they found me and I had to go back. It forced me to face the consequences of what I had done. I wanted to take responsibility for my actions. I wanted to grow up and do what I could to make things right.'"

"How did that make you feel?" Caroline wondered.

"I don't know. I guess I was surprised but what really surprised me was when he told me he was shocked when he got back and found that I was gone. He said he didn't know what to do. He was desperate to be there for me in any way he could, so he came up with the plan to get Jane to help get in touch with me. He said, 'Please believe me, Beth. I wanted to be there for you. I wanted to come see you, but Jane told me your father had forbidden you to have anything to do with me and I knew there was no way I could get to Illinois.'

"I was crying so hard by that point. Just the fact that he had wanted to be with me when I had all these years thought he didn't care about me. Then he added, 'I know you probably thought now that I was back in school, I had just picked up where I had left off. But you're so wrong, Beth, everything was changed. I struggled to get through each day and not let anyone know the turmoil I felt inside for what I had caused. I was a hollow shell of myself and the guilt and shame I felt for what I had done was almost impossible to live with.'"

"So, he was living the same life of Hell you were. What did you say?" Caroline said.

"I held nothing back. I told him of my horrors, my fears, my pain for having been abandoned. I made sure he could appreciate how guilty I had felt. I wanted him to know how lonely I was without a family and most of all without him. How awful it was to be banished from my home, my school, my friends. I was crying so hard; the same kind of hard like the day I got off the plane and couldn't see where I was going. Twenty-five years of pain poured out of me in torrents. All those feelings I had locked inside me. I was doubled over in my chair."

Caroline and Sarah both started to cry, feeling Beth's acute pain.

"Do you think Jack heard you?" asked Sarah.

"I know he did because he got up from his seat and walked over to kneel on the ground beside my chair. He reached up and took my hand in his and kissed it, then wiped away his tears. He reached up with his other hand and brushed my tears away, then put his arm around me. He said, 'I know I don't have a right to ask for your forgiveness that my cowardness has caused you. I was so selfish to choose a career at the Air Force Academy over the responsibility I should have assumed.'"

"Do you think you can forgive him, Beth? He hurt as much as you did. I think it's so sad to think you had such strong feelings for each other and you've both been hurting for so many years because of them."

"I think I can forgive him, Caroline. But I had to say one more thing. I stood up and looked him in the eye. 'The deepest pain I had to endure was because you abandoned me and didn't love me enough to stand by me.'"

"I can't stand it, Beth. What did he say?"

"Sarah, he waited a few seconds and I didn't think he was going to say anything. He just seemed deep in thought, then he put his hands on my arms and said, 'You're wrong, Beth. I'd never had feelings for anyone like those I had for you. I knew I couldn't have my career and be a husband and father. I made the wrong choice. It wasn't that I didn't love you enough. I loved you too much.'"

"Did you cry when he said he loved you too much?" sobbed Caroline caught up in the moment.

"We held each other and cried together for a long time. I didn't want to leave him, but it seemed all was said that had to be said. He walked me to the car and was concerned that I was alright to drive, which I assured him I was. I told him I never say 'goodbye' but instead just thanked him for the chance to talk and wished him well."

1998

The next few years passed quickly. Children went off to college; the women aged, one or two went on a diet once, twice or three times-or not; cut their hair then let it grow long and cut it again; went from dresses to pant suits and finally slacks; gave up wearing spiked heels and continued to meet on Wednesday nights, still finding comfort in their friendship and grateful for their soft place.

Beth, having faced her demons with the help of her therapist for six years, realized that it wasn't fair to Ed to remain married. They divorced amicably and within a year, Beth was relieved to learn Ed was seeing another woman and appeared to be happy.

Caroline and Steve moved to the lake where they played golf and tennis on weekends using activity to diminish the tension that was always in the background of their marriage. Steve never resumed attending AA meetings and abandoned his connection with the young man he had befriended years ago. Caroline continued to enjoy her work and build her career. On weekends, she and Steve enjoyed baking homemade apple pies together on wintry Saturday afternoons or just sitting by the fire in their recliners, reading. They no longer danced but enjoyed peaceful moments taking the dinghy out at dusk for a trip around the lake. Caroline held onto those times praying that her suspicions about Steve were all in her imagination, until one night in early 1998, Caroline arrived at knitting, anxious to speak with Beth and Sarah. She walked over and gave each a hug as soon as she walked in.

"Caroline, I told Sarah you were staying with me, but I didn't want to betray your confidentiality so I didn't really explain why or what happened."

"Thanks, Beth. I can't say as I'm surprised by what happened on Saturday, because I've just had this feeling that something was going on with Steve, but I didn't know what it was. Ever since the rehab center, he has just seemed different; more distant, more agitated. Any time I've tried to talk to him, he would either tell me everything was fine or snap at me and say he had a headache or some other excuse."

"Did he start drinking again, Caroline?" Sarah asked.

"No, but he was starting to get so irritable, I wasn't sure I could trust that there wouldn't be another incident like what happened with the ax. I wasn't feeling safe. It's been our Wednesday nights when I felt the safest. On Saturday, I made an appointment to get my hair cut and was so relieved to be out of the house, I decided to grab a sandwich and do some shopping. We had planned that night to play tennis with our group out of town, but when I arrived home mid- afternoon, I knew I had plenty of time to pack. I walked into the cabin and was immediately confronted by Steve. He sneered at me demanding to know where I was and what had taken me so long. I calmly told him I had gone to the hairdresser and, since it was such a nice day, and not having much opportunity to shop, had grabbed a sandwich and poked around in the shops."

"Caroline, don't tell me he came after you again?" Sarah asked, horrified.

"No, but my explanation did nothing to calm him. He was livid. I watched as he walked over to my dog and picked him up by the tail, dangling him in the air. I screamed and told him to put him down. I was so angry I was ready to call the police."

"Oh my God, is your dog alright?" asked Sarah.

"Yes, he put the dog down and then slowly walked across the room toward me, picking up a small wooden chair on the way. As he walked toward me, he slowly lifted the chair over his head to hit me. I was so angry; I didn't even think before I stepped forward and stopped him in his tracks. I was so livid, probably because deep down I was frightened and angry about my dog; but I'd had it. There was no way I was going to allow him to treat me this way anymore. Without even considering what could happen to me, I walked up to him, pointed my finger within inches of his face and said through gritted teeth, 'Don't you dare!'"

"What did he do?" Sarah asked, sitting on the edge of her seat.

"He lowered the chair. I walked calmly into the bedroom. Steve yelled to me that he didn't feel like playing tennis that night and I could find a substitute. I breathed a sigh of relief and didn't answer. I quietly took a suitcase and began filling it. Steve thought I was packing for the evening of tennis so he didn't question what I was doing. But I was in our bedroom frantically packing enough to get me out of the house, hoping Steve wouldn't walk in. I wasn't sure what either of you were doing but hoped one of you could let me stay the night. I just knew it was the end. I was glad Beth picked up when I called. Just like I tried to tell the hospital people, even though Steve hadn't touched alcohol since that night, the psychological problems were still an issue. I was not going to put myself in danger any longer."

"I'm glad you got out of there, Caroline." Sarah was visibly relieved.

"I walked back through the living room and out the door, right past Steve but neither of us said a word. Once I got in the car, I collapsed. I pulled out of the driveway so fast and started to drive down the highway, crying and sitting in the car alone, screaming in pain hoping the screaming would ease the pit in my stomach. It didn't. My stomach was in knots. I had to keep swallowing to keep from vomiting my lunch. Beth, I don't know what I would have done if you were away that night but I know I could have called you too Sarah."

"Did Steve try and reach you?"

"No, but I felt I owed him the courtesy of knowing I wasn't coming back that night, so when I reached Beth's, I called and left a message. I received a call the next day from Steve telling me I was never to enter the house again. I had packed one dress when I left and knew I needed my clothes, but was afraid to go back to the cabin alone."

"I'm glad I was home, Caroline, when you called. You know you're welcome to stay with me as long as it takes to figure out what you want to do."

"The only thing I know right now is that I need to get my clothes for work but I'm afraid to go back to the cabin alone. I've been thinking of a plan that I think will work. Would one of you be able to drive with me to the cabin and just stand outside while I go in?"

"Do you think that's safe, Caroline? What if he comes after you? Sarah asked with concern.

"I know he doesn't want me there, so I'm thinking if I could borrow some empty suitcases from you both, I'll bring them, walk in and he'll think I'm coming back. If I scream, then you call the police."

The next day, both Sarah and Beth accompanied Caroline to the cabin and waited outside while Caroline did exactly what she said she was going to do. When she walked in, they heard Steve scream, 'Get out of here!' They listened while Caroline explained she needed her clothes, and if she couldn't get them, she had no choice but to move back in. As quickly as she could, she stuffed every bit of clothing and toiletries into the three suitcases, dragged them across the floor and out the door.

Once in the car again with Beth and Sarah, Caroline sobbed, "When it was good, it was so good. When it was bad, it was so very bad."

They drove to Beth's in silence.

Over the coming weeks, Sarah continued to try and assert herself with Rick and reclaim her sense of self. She noticed that Rick seemed to be fearful of no longer being needed as the provider in the family and seemed depressed, napping often. He seemed angry and irritable; seldom calling Sarah any longer during his day at work. Rick's change in personality was disturbing to Sarah, who reported one Wednesday night, "His anger is usually directed at me, but I've noticed he also snaps at our children, as well. It's been a struggle to find our place in the marriage now. I try continually to show him that he is still loved and needed. He's just unable to see that I could want some space and still love and need him. When he comes after me with his anger, I know in my heart he doesn't mean it. He always apologizes soon after and says he's going to go take a nap. I'm just thankful that I have a soft place to land here in the loft because there are some days that are more difficult to get through than others."

Beth was a different woman. She seemed to Sarah and Caroline to have finally found peace; emotionally healthy at last. She was absorbed with her position as an elementary school principal and shared with the women one Wednesday that she had finally spoken with her children and was free at last from the fear of them finding out about her past.

"Last night, I pulled my children into the living room and told them about the baby. I felt they were old enough to know the truth about what my father had always called my 'indiscretion'.

"What was their reaction? I'm sure they were surprised." Caroline said.

"They reacted differently than I would have thought, but I sensed they didn't judge me. My son asked me where the baby was and I told him I didn't know. My daughter asked if I was going to try and find my son. I told her no; I didn't want to interfere with my son's life. It felt so good to get it out in the open, as though I had crossed another milestone in my healing."

"Good, I'm glad that's over for you, Beth, and even more relieved that they accepted what you said without thinking any less of you. I'm sure that's a tremendous relief."

1999

On the third Wednesday night in January, 1999, the women gathered. Sarah and Caroline noticed Beth's hands were shaking badly, her eyes were swollen and she looked pale.

Concerned, Sarah asked if Beth was feeling well.

"Monday night, the kids and I had just had dinner. Two of my kids were home and had gone to their rooms to do their homework. I was just finishing up the dinner dishes when the phone rang. I answered it and was asked, 'Is this Beth?' I replied, 'Yes. Who's calling please?' The man on the line answered and I gasped; my heart was pounding in my chest."

"Who was it? Your son?" Caroline asked hopefully.

"I struggled to keep calm but felt everything seemed to be coming at me. I couldn't even speak. The man on the other end of the line said he was from Illinois and was my child's adopted brother."

"Oh my God, Beth, what did you say?"

"Sarah, I couldn't speak. My knees were weak I thought I would pass out. I was standing in the kitchen leaning on the counter for support, afraid of what I was going to hear. I was confused about why this man was calling me, but he explained he was asked to make the initial call to see if I would be willing to talk to my son by phone."

"What did you say?" Both couldn't wait to hear Beth's answer.

"I said 'Yes' and he said he would call me the next night; that is, last night. I don't know how I got through yesterday. I hung up and began pacing around the house like it was on fire. I couldn't stop moving. I was scared, excited, and worried; once more terrified of what this meant for my future. I had finally put my past to rest, found peace and here everything was all coming back at me. I couldn't sleep."

"I don't know how you got through the twenty-four hours, Beth. I think I would have been paralyzed, and you even went to work!"

"The call came around six-thirty and was from the same man who had called the night before."

"So, this was just last night?" Sarah clarified.

"Yes. I was surprised because I was expecting a call from my son, certainly not another call from his brother. He told me that his brother had been searching for me for years but adoption records were sealed in the state of Illinois, making it impossible to locate me until a few months ago; actually, last November twentieth. He went on to say that same day, while my son was on a business trip in Europe, a letter had arrived in the mail containing a copy of his birth certificate with my name, the Illinois courts having just ruled to open adoption records. I listened without saying a word. Then my son's brother said, 'I'm so very sorry to have to tell you this. Your son was killed on that same day in a small plane crash.' All alone in the kitchen, I screamed. I wailed, barely able to breathe."

"Oh Beth; the pain. I cannot imagine how much you hurt."

"The brother waited on the line. I don't know how long it was before I could speak, but I was angry. I asked him, 'Why did you bother to call me if he was gone?' He explained that my son's widow urged him to find me to fulfill the dream of her husband's life. He went on to explain further that my son and his wife had two children. My son's widow wanted to speak with me, and in her grief saw me as a connection to him as they had loved each other so much and she was beside herself with grief. He asked if she could write to me. I answered 'Yes'."

"It just seems like your hurt can't ever heal, Beth. It seems like every time you pick yourself up, you seem to get hit again with something else. I'm so sorry," lamented Sarah.

"For years I had longed to find my child, to see him, know him, and hear about his life. All the years I had imagined meeting him somewhere. Never in my imagination did I ever dream I would hear he was dead. It's hard to accept that he's gone and I'll never see or know him."

"Are you sure the man was telling you the truth? You don't think it's a crank or scam, do you?"

"Caroline, I wanted to think so but I Googled the date of the accident and it was exactly as he said. I'm hurting so much."

Beth's news cast a solemn mood in the room. There were no words to ease the pain. Caroline thought perhaps it would help if she could change the subject and offer some help to Sarah, who continued to try and disengage herself from Rick's overpowering caretaking.

"Now that my divorce is final and I've got extra time on my hands, I heard about this new website where anyone can sell items and people bid on them. It's called eBay and I've been playing around with it for the past few weeks. It's fairly easy to do and exciting when you get someone bidding on your item or even better, when it sells. Yesterday, I sold a very expensive antique that I didn't want any more and got more for it than I paid."

Sarah's interest was piqued.

"How does it work, Caroline? I'm pretty good with a computer and I've got collections that have been packed away for years in boxes in a closet upstairs. I'd love to learn how to do it if you have the time to teach me."

"What kinds of collections?" Caroline asked.

"I've got over one hundred Swatch watches for one thing and some of them are old and I think collectibles now. I've got French pocketbooks that I know are valued now."

"Okay, the first thing you have to do is take a picture of whatever you want to sell. The more pictures the better. Make sure the picture shows the Swatch name. I'll come over on Saturday and we can do some listing. I'll set up an account for you and help you with the descriptions. Then you just wait until someone bids or buys!"

Sarah was excited and couldn't wait to get started. The next morning over coffee, Sarah told Rick about eBay and her new venture. For some reason to her surprise, he wasn't threatened and seemed a little excited for her.

On Saturday Caroline came over and helped Sarah create a few listings; her first was a popular patterned Swatch. Sarah scheduled the auction to launch on Monday. Two days later, Sarah arrived at knitting group so upset she was barely able to speak.

"I am so upset; no, I'm furious!" Sarah fumed.

Both women waited for Sarah to continue.

"I launched my first eBay auction and watched it on the first day. On the second day, I received an email that my watch had sold and I was so excited. I couldn't believe it. I had made money; my own money; I had earned my own money."

"That's great, Sarah. Congratulations! Isn't it fun?"

"I was so happy and I went on the website to create the label to ship it and send an email to the buyer thanking him or her and giving them a tracking number. I was shocked and devastated to discover that the buyer was Rick! I had been so excited and he ruined it. I am so upset."

"What? Why did he do that? Did you confront him when he got home?"

"No, I phoned Rick at work and questioned why he had done what he had. He told me that he thought I would enjoy having some money I had earned myself. He didn't get it. I hadn't earned it myself. He stole those feelings of joy and accomplishment away from me. I was so angry, and I got really sarcastic with him. I asked him, 'Where do you want the watch shipped?' He laughed and didn't even get it."

"Did you tell him to stay away from your eBay account?"

"No, I didn't say anything. I thought my sarcasm would let him know I was angry. But about three hours later, I sold another watch and was worried that Rick had bought it but was relieved when I went in and checked and the buyer ID was not Rick's. I was really excited that I had sold another watch; a real sale this time. This morning I went into my account to get the watch ready to ship and saw that a question had come in the day before about shipping costs, but the question had already been answered."

"Did you answer Sarah's email, Caroline?"

"No, it wasn't Caroline. I knew she wouldn't ever do that without asking me first, so, I questioned Rick. He nonchalantly said he happened to be on my account and noticed I had a message. He assured me he thought he could be helpful if he answered it. The response which should have been penned by me was written by Rick in his words. It didn't even sound like anything I would have written. Again, I was livid and felt violated."

"Why don't you change your password, Sarah? That way he can't access your account." Beth suggested.

"No, I don't want to do that to Rick. He's already feeling out of place with my new attitude. I'll just wait and see if over time, he gets tired of my eBay activity and leaves me alone. His interference has taken the joy out of my online selling though. I don't even know if I want to keep listing on eBay."

Beth suggested. "I don't think you should let Rick ruin your opportunity for you to do something for yourself."

"I agree," added Caroline. "You're finally finding yourself and it's too important for you to let him get in your way."

The following week, Beth arrived with a large Manilla folder in her hand. As soon as everyone sat down, she pulled out an eight- page letter from her son's widow which she read aloud. The woman spoke of her husband, Beth's son, as a young man, and a husband and father to their three young children. She painted a picture which allowed Beth to glow with pride not only because of the wonderful man he must have been but that he had been given a wonderful life; much better than she could have provided. She chronicled his life with pictures. There were pictures from childhood, his teenage years, skiing as a young adult, college graduation, wedding pictures and finally pictures of him holding each of his children.

Sarah sat with an expression of surprise.

"Isn't it weird, Beth? Just like when you were a baby and your father wasn't there, he got to see you grow through photographs your mother shared. Now you're getting to see your son's life in the same way because you couldn't be there."

As the pictures were passed around. Sarah and Caroline had many questions.

"Listening to your journey, Beth, I feel as though I want to know this child too." Caroline said.

"Do you see any resemblance? Who does he look like? Who do his children look like?"

"I think his daughter has my eyes and his son has Jack's mouth and jaw. I think our son looks a little like my brother but has Jack's eyes and forehead."

"How are you going to respond to the letter?"

"I feel as though I want to explain how the baby came to be and the decision which was made in placing him for adoption and why so she understands how young I was and not that I had a choice in keeping the baby. I plan to write her a letter this weekend but I'm not sure I can handle or am strong enough to form a relationship with them. I think it might be different if my son was still living, but I don't know what I could offer."

"I'm sure once you've gotten over the shock, Beth, you'll do what you feel in your heart is right. But I can see how hard it might be for you to blend both families."

"I definitely want her to know that we were teenagers who had both suffered for years because of one night. I want her to know that I had tried to search for him years ago but the records had not been unsealed back then."

On the following Wednesday, Beth brought a letter she had received from her son's adoptive mother which she read aloud to Sarah and Caroline. Her son's adoptive mother thanked Beth for sharing her child with her and she wanted to share him with Beth. In her lengthy letter, she recounted stories from his childhood, the happiness he had brought to the family and assured Beth that he was a special child and an even greater man. The women had tears in their eyes once Beth finished.

"I've been thinking this past week, Beth, about what you and Jack agreed. You told us how that day on the hill, if either one of you heard from the child or knew something, you would share it. Are you going to let him know?" Caroline asked.

"I've been thinking of that too. It has been so many years; I can't see that it serves any purpose. I'm sure Jack has moved on with life and I'm not sure it's fair to stir up his life."

'It just seems like your hurt can't ever heal, Beth. It seems like every time you pick yourself up, you seem to get hit again with something else. I'm so sorry' lamented Sarah.

"I just want to hold on to the peacefulness I've finally found. I just want to leave the past in the past. I go back and forth about trying to put my new family out of my mind then I think about boarding a plane and flying to California to meet them."

After much consideration, Beth decided to leave the past in the past although she received a Christmas card with a photo of her two grandchildren and their mother the following year.

Early in 2001, Beth shared that she had received an email inviting her to a fortieth-year high school reunion in June.

"That's exciting. Do you think Jack will be there?" Sarah asked.

"I don't know. I wondered the same thing. I guess I'll find out. I'm definitely going."

"I think we're so fortunate to have Wednesday nights. I don't know what I would have done without the two of you over the years. We've sure come a long way, haven't we?' Caroline reminisced.

"I don't want to do anything to jeopardize our group, but I want to ask you both something," Beth said. "Last Monday I was on the way to buy groceries and stopped at the yarn shop to pick up a new pattern for a baby blanket for my cousin. At the back of the shop, I noticed two women trying to choose a color of yarn and having a hard time making a decision. They turned and asked me for my opinion. Anyway, one lady introduced herself as Jenny, and the other said her name was Lexi."

"They thanked me for offering my opinion, then asked me, 'Have you been knitting long?' I told them I had been knitting for what seemed like my entire life. Jenny told me she had been knitting for years also and was fairly certain she could be classified as an addict! Lexi said she had knit since she was a teenager. I mentioned our Wednesday nights and both immediately said they would love to have a group like ours.

"I wanted to make sure they understood we don't always just knit. I explained that sometimes it's just a good excuse for a night out of the house, but over the almost twenty years we had been meeting, we've become very close and supportive of one another. I thought I should clarify, in case I had misled or misrepresented the group as just a knitting circle. 'We do knit!' I exclaimed 'but sometimes it's more than that. Sometimes we just talk about things in our lives or use the group for advice about some things. We've traveled together for so many years, we think of our group as 'a soft place to land.' I smiled when Jenny and Lexi assured me that sounded even better. I asked for their phone numbers but told them I needed to talk to both of you first. I think you'll like them."

The next Wednesday, Beth introduced Jenny and Lexi to the women and two more chairs were pulled up to the circle. Beth, Caroline and Sarah explained how they had met and the group had started almost twenty years ago.

"Where did you meet your husband, Sarah?" Jenny asked.

"We met in college and I've always been a stay at home mom, but Caroline taught me how to sell online, and I'm struggling to exert my independence from my husband who has always taken care of me and never allowed me to do anything for myself. It's not easy, but I think it's getting better."

"I'm the youngest of seven children", Lexi said, "and I know just what you mean, Sarah, with a husband who wants to be a caregiver. I married my childhood sweetheart, actually a boy I met in eighth grade. I never dated anyone else. My parents liked him and encouraged us to get married which we did thirty years ago. He told me he didn't want me working so I've been a stay at home mother too. We have three children who are all off and in their own apartments with good jobs. I've got a lot of time on my hands so I knit and read but that gets old."

"Beth and Caroline, do you work?" Jenny asked. "I've been an elementary school principal for a few years, have four children and am divorced." Beth answered. Caroline shared, "My husband and I were recently divorced and I have three children from a previous marriage. I'm a national sales consultant with a publishing company."

Jenny shared, "I have two children. I've been married for thirty-five years to a good man. We met when I was eighteen and dated for a few years. I knew I had found a wonderful guy. When he asked me to marry him after two years, I couldn't say 'Yes' fast enough. Looking back,

I know now how young I was. I kind of had a tough time growing up, really without a father and with a mother who had problems. I knew right away Matt would treat me better than my father had treated me and I wouldn't end up in life like my mother. She is so bitter."

Caroline assured Jenny, "One thing you'll learn here is that we listen, we care and support each other and what we talk about in this room, we keep confidential. Any time you want to share Jenny, and you too Lexi if you ever want to talk about anything, we're here."

Jenny shared, "I'm the eldest of three children. When I was seven years old, my mother divorced my father claiming he abused her. My mother moved us in with my grandmother but told us we were only going to stay there until we could get settled. Whatever that meant? My mother was more interested in her new boyfriend than she was in any of us kids, so I looked at my grandmother as the only adult in my life who cared. We stayed with her for about a year and then my mother got her own apartment."

"Where was your father?", Sarah asked.

"The only time we saw my father was for a few weeks in the summer. The rest of the year, we never saw or heard from him. My mother was a bartender and worked nights so my grandmother took care of us when we were little, but when I got to be thirteen, my mother met a man named Jim and he took care of us. At first, we thought it was nice to have a man in the house since we didn't have a father. He used to make us dinner, watch tv with us and horse around with us.

"What started out at first as roughhousing and wrestling around the floor with Jim though, suddenly turned into tickling and I didn't like it. It made me uncomfortable because a lot of times, he would accidently touch me, especially my chest. I knew it wasn't right but I didn't' know what to do about it. I told my mother and she blamed me. My mother told me to, 'Be nice to him and make him feel welcome', so I told my grandmother."

"What did your grandmother say?" Caroline asked.

"I told my grandmother but she just told me to not pay any attention I think maybe my grandmother said something to Jim because almost immediately, Jim packed his bags and left. Within weeks, there was another man my mother brought home. This went on for years until my mother became pregnant with her final boyfriend and married him. They had a girl, my stepsister, and right after that, my stepfather took everything and left. I remember my mother crying; I just locked myself in my room. It went on like that for years; one boyfriend moving in after another."

"What did you do, Jenny, when all these boyfriends kept moving in and out?"

"Lexi, I just stayed locked in my room at night until I was eighteen and got a job at the library in town, which put me out of the house and away from her boyfriends. Not long after I started working there, I met Matt who had just finished college and was working part-time until he figured out what he wanted to do. He was interested in starting a business. He began coming into the library often at first and then within a month, every night. We started going out and I knew I had finally found a man in my life I could trust."

"Did he know about your mother and her boyfriends?", Beth wondered.

"Yes, I had told him. My mother knew I was dating someone, but never cared about anything I did. She was too interested in her boyfriends. Out of the blue, one night I was leaving for work and my mother announced we were moving. She told me where we were moving to, then said, 'I'm not moving your things. You can move your own things.'"

"What was her problem? So, what happened?" Sarah asked incredulously.

"She was just bitter and I think she was angry because she knew I had met Matt and was jealous. When I got home from work that night, the apartment was empty except for my things. I didn't know what to do or who to turn to for help, so I called Matt."

"Thank goodness you had him, Jenny."

"Matt immediately said, 'Don't worry. I'll take care of it.' There was no way I was going to move into my mother's new apartment, so I moved in with Matt. Within the year, he asked me to marry him. We were married within a month with just Matt's parents there and we stayed with them until Matt could get his hardware business started and we could afford to live on our own. Within four years we had two children."

The evening ended with the sense that Jenny and Lexi had been with the group for years. The next few weeks the women talked about dogs as Jenny's children were begging her for a dog, what book each was reading and what vacation plans everyone had.

Months later, Jenny came to knitting group holding a letter she had received that morning. Her hands were shaking as she poured herself a diet Coke, taking it to her seat.

"I know I told you about my mother the first time I met you. I've not heard from my mother for years even though I had tried to reach out to her and Matt had gone out of his way to be kind to her and support me when I was continually rejected by her. He can't understand why my mother isn't even interested in her grandchildren. Well, this morning, I went to the mailbox and pulled out this letter."

Jenny read the letter to the women who were all shocked at its contents and unable to fathom what had precipitated such a letter.

Beth assured Jenny, "It doesn't sound as though your mother's letter was as a result of anything you did. How can a mother say to her daughter that she wants nothing to do with her?"

"I'm not surprised. My mother has been emotionally detached for years and has never shown any interest in my life or my children. Somehow though there's a finality seeing the ink on the paper. I didn't know if I really wanted to come to knitting tonight, but the more I thought about it, if there was anywhere, I could find a soft place to land, it was here. I knew I could count on all of you to understand."

"Did your mother ever see her grandchildren or come to visit?" Beth asked.

"Yes, we invited her to come visit over the years but it seemed each visit ended in angry words. I think she saw how Matt treated me and it made her angry. I had what she always wanted. Even when my brother, Rob, died suddenly of a heart attack four years ago, I was out doing errands. When I got home, the button was blinking on the answer machine and when I pushed the button, I heard the message, 'Hello Jenny. It's Mom. Rob died.'"

"Did you go the funeral?"

"Yes, Matt and I took the children and flew out, but we were greeted with a chilly welcome from my mother. When we were leaving, she never came downstairs to even say goodbye. Two years later, my stepsister died of a drug overdose, and we went to her funeral, but again we were ignored. I've tried to keep checking up on Mom over the years, but not anymore."

Jenny sobbed as she read the last words from her mother's letter, 'Have a good life.'

The women on either side of Jenny reached out and squeezed her hand as Sarah, her closest friend in the group, said, "Jenny, you can't blame yourself for your mother's problems." The others in the room consoled Jenny with kind words.

"Your mother's problems aren't your fault," Caroline remarked.

"Your mother resented you because you have a wonderful home and a husband who loves and cherishes you." Lexi commented.

Beth added, "My mother died a long time ago and I've missed her and wished I had one more chance to talk to her. Do you think you'll regret not contacting her after she's gone?"

Jenny replied with sadness, "No. She left me a long time ago."

When Jenny ended, Sarah shared, I feel your sadness. I had a wonderful grandmother who I've talked about for years with Beth and Caroline. I have wonderful memories of weekends spent in my grandmother's kitchen and garden. I'm sorry you don't have those kinds of memories with your mother or your grandmother."

On a lighter note, Lexi asked, "Is anyone having trouble sleeping more than six or seven hours a night?" which was met with nods of agreement from all.

"Anyone have any suggestions for hair loss?" Sarah threw out to the group.

They each agreed it was a common problem. "Just keep your hair short," Jenny said, "And invest in a hair spray company."

"I sold six more watches in the past week and I'm getting a lot of interest on eBay with my French purse collection. I love having my own money! It has taken me so long to convince Rick to let this be mine, but I think when I said to him a while ago, 'I understand you want to help me be successful. But I can't feel successful unless I do it myself. I have to fail or succeed on my own.' I think he finally got it."

As June approached, Beth began to feel some anxiety about her high school reunion in two weeks.

"I'm excited about going and touching base with friends, but I'm a little nervous if Jack is going to be there." Beth turned to Lexi and Jenny and added, "Jack's my old high school boyfriend and we have quite a history. It's been almost twenty years since we last spoke and I have no idea how he'll react to me if he's there."

Nothing else was mentioned. Lexi and Jenny respected Beth's right to privacy.

They laughed as each shared a memory of their high school years and even high school boyfriends.

The women loved to listen to Lexi's stories. As the youngest of seven children, she had plenty to share which usually left the group in peals of laughter so the women were surprised when Lexi one Wednesday said,

"Jenny, when you were talking about your mother's boyfriend touching you inappropriately, it brought back terrible memories for me but I didn't want to talk about it then. When I was a kid, my older brother would sometimes take me into the attic at night and touch me. One night my mother even walked in."

"What did she do?" Jenny asked. "I hope she did more than my mother did."

"My mother didn't do anything. She ignored it but when I got to be eighteen, I did the same thing you did, Jenny. I got married and left. My parents liked Brian so they were happy and I thought I would be too, but there were a couple of things my husband said that have stayed with me since the day we were married. One comment was the day after our wedding. He asked me, 'Did you notice my mother's gloves? Weren't they pretty?' I ignored the question but silently wished I would hear, 'You looked pretty' which he never spoke and being overweight, it was something I really needed to hear."

To the ladies in the group, Lexi was the epitome of the happy wife of a successful corporate CEO with a publicly published annual income in excess of one million dollars. She lived in a large home with a built-in swimming pool and was the mother of three grown successful children. Her husband convinced her that it didn't look good for a CEO to have a wife who worked and assured her he would provide for her and further, he wanted her time available to him.

Lexi said, "He also added, 'As I climb up the corporate ladder, there will be social obligations you'll be expected to attend with me and working will get in the way of that'. As the youngest of seven children and always having to help my mother around the house, the thought of a husband who expected little of me, other than to maintain the house, raise our children and be available to him, sounded heavenly."

"It does sound nice, Lexi." Caroline agreed.

"I thought it would be, but I have nothing of my own. I have a credit card but when the bill comes in, Brian goes through every line asking me questions about where I was or what I bought. It's maddening! I have no access to cash but I came up with a way a few years ago, and he hasn't discovered it. When I go grocery shopping, I write the check for ten dollars more than the groceries, so I have some cash. If I meet someone for coffee or lunch, I have to ask them to pay so he can't track where I've been or there's Hell to pay."

"Have you ever given him any reason to distrust you?" Jenny asked.

"Never, but he is always accusing me of having an affair. Look at me, ladies! I'm so overweight. My nickname used to be Pudge. Do I look like someone who is having an affair? Three weeks ago, I came home from the store and discovered he had put a video camera in the bedroom to catch me!"

"That is so weird. Do you say anything to him?"

"Of course, Beth. He didn't even bother answering. I feel like a prisoner in my own house. He controls everything with money, even our children. He pays for their apartments, buys them cars and anytime I threaten to leave, he tells me our children will have nothing to do with me because they know who has the money and they're financially dependent on him."

"I am shocked, Lexi. I never would have guessed your life was like that. You always seem so happy and are joking about everything," Beth remarked.

"It's all a front and probably why I look the way I do. He told me not long ago when I threatened to leave, 'If you leave me not only will you lose your children, but if they ever have children, you'll never see your grandchildren."

"What a hurtful, spiteful thing to say, Lexi," said Beth.

"I thought when we were first married and he seemed jealous, it was flattering but now I'm angry. I am furious that I am controlled, monitored, and not allowed to invite friends to the house. Yet, four or five times a week, he expects me to have sex and it's easier just to give in than argue."

"How do you get through it?"

"How do you think, Jenny. I transport my mind somewhere else until it's over."

"What happens if you say no?"

"Then, he doesn't speak to me for days, eats and leaves the dirty dishes and mess for me to wash. He ignores me completely on weekends and goes off to play golf both Saturday and Sunday."

"Do you really mind if he plays golf all weekend? I would think that would be a relief."

"It is, Beth, but it's lonely too. We often have to travel to corporate meetings which are usually somewhere warm and he goes off to play leaving me in the hotel or at the pool. I escape into a make-believe world of books and picked up knitting again. I'm so thankful I found you all. I don't know how I could continue to cope without what you all call, this soft place to land."

"I'm glad I happened to stop at the yarn shop that day, Lexi. We're glad you're here with us. You keep talking about your weight. You have such a pretty face; I didn't really pay much attention to your weight."

Lexi thanked Beth for the compliment and added, "I think I'm so angry and I use food for comfort. Every time I go on a diet, it never lasts. I exercise quite a bit, lose weight, give up and start again."

"I think we can all sympathize with that!" Caroline confessed.

"I'm most embarrassed when I have to go to these corporate convention dinners where wives are smartly dressed in expensive outfits, and I'm worried if I can fit in the dining room chair."

"Have you ever thought of going for therapy, Lexi? Caroline and Sarah both know that I was in therapy for a lot of years and will agree with me, that it has helped tremendously. It was the answer to a lot of problems I had."

"I'd like the name of your therapist, Beth. I'm willing to try."

A week later, the women could hardly wait to hear how Beth's high school reunion had gone. Before even sitting down, Sarah urged Beth to tell them and not to leave out a single detail!

"I was a little late getting to the restaurant, partly because I couldn't decide what to wear and for the hour before I was supposed to go, kept thinking maybe I shouldn't go. By the time I got there, I missed the cocktail hour where everyone had been mingling which was too bad because I didn't get to speak with anyone."

"Was Jack there?" Sarah asked, hardly able to control her curiosity.

"Yes. I walked through the door into this beautiful room overlooking the water and spotted him immediately leaning against another door just inside the room. It reminded me of the time I walked into that party a long time ago."

"Did he see you?" Sarah wondered.

"Yes. He finished talking and immediately walked over to greet me. I wasn't sure what to expect so I held out my hand, but, just like before, he gave me a warm smile and nice hug. There wasn't much time to talk and not privacy, but we quickly caught up on our children and lives in the last twenty years. Jack explained he was still flying, had downsized to a small house after selling the house on the river and was filling his spare time by writing."

"Were you nervous?"

"A little, but I was happy to see him."

"He did most of the talking. He told me he had published three books so far and then asked me if I was with anyone."

"I told him that I was still divorced and still in education and I that I enjoyed writing, too. I jokingly told him I had been working on a novel which I referred to as 'the next New York Times Best Seller'. He laughed and bantered, 'I wonder who will end up publishing more books. We'll have to keep track.' Dinner was announced and we each moved in different directions, reconnecting with classmates."

"Do you think he meant anything when he said, 'We'll have to keep track?' Sarah asked.

"I don't think so but I was aware of his presence in the room the whole night. Every time I glanced over at him; he would quickly glance away from me. I had the feeling he would have liked to spend more time together, but it never happened. At the end of the night, I asked for his address and explained I wanted to send something to him. He looked a little puzzled, but didn't ask why. We hugged each other goodbye and that was it."

Caroline and Sarah, knowing what Beth was alluding to, both nodded indicating their agreement that Beth was doing the right thing.

July 2001

Dear Jack,

It was good to see you at the reunion even though we didn't have much opportunity to speak. Seeing you though brought back the memory of sitting with you on the hill and the promise we made to each other.

I remember the day; the yellow sweater you loaned me to wear which hung down to my knees and your kid's boots. You smiled when you saw me, then commented on how cute I looked. That made me smile. While we were sitting on top of that hill, getting to know one another again, we each seemed to dance around the issue of why we were meeting. I'm writing to honor the promise we made to each other that day and to also say I'm sorry.

I've known the truth since one very strange night in January a few years ago. I didn't know where you were living at the time or how to reach you. I thought and hoped you had a new life, a new wife, a new family. I was unsure if I should contact you and reopen a painful wound. I thought perhaps you had started to heal as I had since our last meeting in your garden.

Seeing you last Saturday made me realize that I didn't have the right to make the decision of whether or not you should know. I understood from Jane you deeply regretted the path our lives had taken and after two failed marriages, she relayed you had abandoned all hope of finding someone with whom to share your love and life. I didn't want to cause you more hurt. Unfortunately, our lives are intertwined whether or not we choose them to be.

I'm writing to say I have the information about our child and will leave it up to you if you choose to contact me. I've enclosed my contact information and will wait to hear from you.

I hope what I can share will bring you closure and put an end to the questions we've each struggled with for over forty years. I know in my heart, if I neglect to tell you what I now know, at the end of my life, I will regret denying you the choice.

Much love always,

Beth

Sarah asked if the women would be opposed to including a new member as the owner of the yarn shop had called and mentioned an avid knitter, a regular customer. The customer whose name was Cindy, was someone the shop owner thought we would enjoy. She commented Cindy had a great sense of humor but she didn't want to mention the group without first asking and had merely taken the woman's name and phone number. The vote was to expand the group to six and Sarah was given the go ahead to contact the shop owner.

Two weeks later, the women welcomed Cindy to their circle. It had been almost twenty years since the time Beth, Caroline and Sarah had arranged their first Wednesday night. Many roads had been traveled in that time, hundreds of laughs and tears shared, problems solved, issued pondered – some resolved, others not.

Sarah asked Beth if she had heard from Jack, which she had not. Beth took the opportunity to explain to Cindy she had just been reconnected with her high school boyfriend at a reunion and the women smiled interpreting the comment to mean there might be more.

During the summer, the women continued to meet although some Wednesdays were missed due to vacations until September when they once more gathered.

Sarah and Caroline both announced their eBay sales had skyrocketed over the summer. It was obvious from Sarah's enthusiasm she was much happier and had become more confident. "I finally was able to convince Rick that the greatest gift he could give me was to allow me to fail or succeed. Ironically," she added, "Rick seems more relaxed without the huge responsibility of trying to meet my every need. Now he has more time to do the kinds of things he likes. I know without the support of all of you and help from Caroline, I would not be where I am today!"

Caroline had big news to share as well.

"I've gotten so into antiques and have learned so much, I've made a lot of contacts with fellow antique collectors on the Internet. I spent half the summer antiquing and love it! Last week, I was looking out my kitchen window at a little shed I have behind my house that used to be an old blacksmith shop and got the idea to open an antique shop. I know I can find enough things to put in it. I'm excited!"

"That is so exciting, Caroline! Are you going to give up your job at the publishing company?" Beth asked surprised by Caroline's news.

"No. I'll open on weekends only and keep my consulting position during the week. I talked with a carpenter two weeks ago and he's coming to remodel the building and make it into a shop. It needs a pine floor and real walls; nothing major. It's going to be awesome and I'm going to have the best of both worlds!"

Cindy offered, "My husband and I took the kids for a vacation at a lake in Maine and had a wonderful time. I painted the kitchen which I think looks great but that's about all I did. Oh a few trips to the beach for the day."

Sarah asked Beth, fully expecting to hear Beth had not heard from Jack, but was surprised and excited when Beth answered, "Yes. I just heard from him."

"I'm dying to know what he said. Come on...Beth. Don't keep us hanging!" Sarah begged.

"He started the phone conversation with small talk about the reunion, 'Great to see you. Weren't you surprised at how good everyone looked? You didn't look a day older.', that kind of thing. We talked some more about our classmates and then Jack said, 'I would like to speak with you and learn what you know but I don't think over the phone is the best way. Would you be willing to have dinner with me next weekend.?" Beth related.

"Obviously you're going, right?" Sarah the romantic wanted to know.

"Of course. I'm going to go through with it. I'm going to go through the whole file of letters and photographs and bring them with me."

When Saturday arrived, Jack picked up Beth promptly at 6:30. The restaurant was lovely, quaint, lighted with soft candles, the décor classic black and white. Shortly after cocktails, Beth related the night she received the phone call from their son's step-brother and then the heartache of the second phone call the following night. She went on to paraphrase the contents of the letter she had received from their son's widow after which, noting that Jack's face indicated an interest in hearing more, she reached into her purse and took out one of the pictures of their son and another of his two children - their grandchildren. Jack stared at the photographs.

Beth suspected Jack was doing the same thing she had done; scrutinizing them looking for resemblances to Jack and her and their families. Jack was spending an inordinate amount of time studying the picture of their grandson. Without a sound, he reached into his pocket and removed a handkerchief. Beth sat somewhat stunned, yet moved, when he held the handkerchief first to his mouth and then gently wiped each eye.

Handing the pictures back to her, Jack struggled to speak. "I've been living with a pain I've carried since my divorce years ago. In the middle of my divorce, my former wife, in retaliation, told me our children were not mine. She had been convincing enough that I believed all these years that I was incapable of fathering a child. Looking at our grandson's resemblance to me proves that she lied to me."

Beth confessed, "I'm not strong enough right now to open the door to the past. I know that's selfish but my life is finally on a path where I have some peace. I don't want to have to explain this family to my grandchildren. I simply can't do it. I feel guilty every Christmas when I get a picture holiday card of our grandchildren. I even last year received a letter from our son's widow that our grandson was playing college football in Maryland and did I want to go." Jack nodded indicating he understood how I felt without any sign one way or another what he was going to do.

After dinner, when they pulled into Beth's driveway, Jack leaned toward her.

"Thank you for reaching out to me and sharing. I have a lot to think about and consider. I had a wonderful time tonight as painful as parts of it were. I've enjoyed getting to know a little about you again after all these years. I feel a little bit like I'm home. Isn't that stupid? Can I see you again next weekend regardless of what decision I make about our son's widow and her children?"

The following Wednesday night, Beth knew the women would want to know how the meeting with Jack went. Before they could ask, Beth shared, "Jack and I had a lovely dinner and a warm, honest conversation. It was so good to see him again and he asked if I would be willing to see him again. He told me how much he was enjoying getting to know me again."

Caroline, the eternal romantic, reached into her knitting bag and pulled out a bottle of Chablis! "I came prepared for a celebration! I just had a feeling, Beth, you were going to share good news!"

By Christmas, Caroline expanded her business to include a Website which, with a manual she studied page by page for four months, she pushed a button to launch it, telling the women on Wednesday, "I was excited as I was when I gave birth to my children."

Her shop was a huge success and within a year she had outgrown the small blacksmith shop and relocated to a large six room shop on a main road closer to the village; an ideal spot as many visitors from out of town passed by on weekends. Caroline attended flea markets early in the mornings and gathered goods to sell online; oftentimes out of bed at 4:00 AM on weekday mornings to list items before leaving for work. When the pickers, those who 'scouted' for antiques at shops for resale called, it was usually to say they had a truck load giving her the right of first refusal. Her online business exposed her to collectors all over the country and she often sold larger pieces with a few pictures emailed to potential buyers before she had the antiques off-loaded from her trailer.

One Saturday morning, she was sitting at a table in her shop knitting when a group of three women passed through the door. After greeting Caroline, the women wandered together through the six rooms. Caroline could hear their comments and appreciated immediately that they were all quite knowledgeable about antiques and were long time collectors. One asked her a few questions about various pieces, while another decided she would purchase an 18thC blanket chest with original snipe hinges and blue paint. It was one of Caroline's favorite pieces; she was initially hesitant to part with the chest, but knew she couldn't keep everything she found. She shared how much she loved the piece. The woman purchasing the chest adding she loved the color of the sweater Caroline was knitting.

They started to share information, one identifying herself as Annie and the other Marcy. Annie shared she loves to knit and has tried to talk Marcy into it, but Marcy was not the least bit interested. Caroline smiled, "It's not for everyone", Caroline said, then added "I knit with a group of women Wednesday evenings; we've been meeting for years. If you're interested Annie, I'll ask the others if we have room for one more."

Caroline took Annie's phone number, wrote up the sale of the blanket chest and said she would be in touch. For the last time, the women added another chair to the knitting circle; their group now numbering seven.

Early in November, Caroline told the group, "My elderly father is ill and I'm afraid he is at the end of his life."

The women expressed their sympathy and after determining there was nothing they could do to help, urged Caroline to call if she needed anything. The following week, Caroline desperately needed the comfort of the group, having lost her father the day before.

Caroline was anxious to share what had happened two days prior to his death. "I stayed with him for the final thirty-six hours of his life. Sometimes I stood by his bedside, saying the Lord's Prayer with him; sometimes I simply held his hand for comfort. Sometimes I talked about special memories knowing that, although his eyes were closed and he appeared to be unconscious, there were slight movements and I just know he heard what I was saying. When dinnertime came, a nurse came in and asked me if I wanted anything to eat. I had no appetite I couldn't have swallowed a bit of food. The night seemed to last forever. I left the room only once to go to the ladies' room and sat alone curled in a chair in the corner with a thin blanket and pillow the rest of the time. I couldn't sleep even for a minute. When the sun came up, I quickly walked down the hall to the nurses' station to ask for a cup of coffee, hurrying back for fear my father might realize I wasn't there."

Beth voiced, "I wish you weren't there alone."

"In the early afternoon, just minutes before his final breath, I leaned over and said, 'I'm here Dad. I'm staying with you.' He uttered the only words he had spoken in the thirty-six hours I had been there beside him. 'Thank you', he mumbled. Then I couldn't believe my ears. I heard the words I had longed to hear all my life. For the first time, I heard his final words, 'Good girl' as he took his last breath."

Caroline was sobbing after sharing the pain and joy of hearing her father and being with him as he passed. Every woman in the room cried with her.

"I waited a little bit before I called the nurse to let her know my father had passed. I just wanted to hold his hand a moment longer. I began to gather what few things he had left in the room and within a half hour, I took the bags and left."

"Are there going to be calling hours?" Sarah asked.

"No, but the funeral is on Thursday. My father was over ninety years old and I knew he wouldn't be with us forever, so about six months ago, I started to write his eulogy. My dad had also prepared a pamphlet detailing his many accomplishments for us to distribute at his funeral."

When Caroline shared the pamphlet with the knitting group, they were astonished that one individual could accomplish so much in a lifetime. Beth, after reading it, looked up and commented nonchalantly, "No wonder you always felt your father loved you for what you accomplished, not for just being who you are, Caroline. His accomplishments obviously were very important to him. He must have viewed his self-worth by what he accomplished and judged his love for you based on your accomplishments in the same way."

Caroline was shocked and questioned. "Why hadn't I ever been able to see that? I had never connected my father's sense of self to the importance of his accomplishments. I know he was always proud of what I had accomplished in my life, and I just wanted him to show me how he loved me just for being me. I wanted him to be proud of me for who I was; my intelligence, my ability to care for others, my sense of humor, my interests, my creativity, my warmth, my smile."

Sarah tried to console Caroline. "I think your father showed his love for you in ways which were meaningful for him so, to his thinking, he was showing his love by pushing you to do better."

"I'm dumbfounded. I'm sitting here thinking about what I've done all my life and the decisions I made; the drive to earn better grades, achieve more college degrees, marry the man he thought I should marry, buy a bigger house. The fact that my father wasn't able to show his love in the ways I needed most, I'm sure is why I was drawn to Steve who, in good times, was capable of demonstrating his affection in a way that made me feel loved for the first time.

"Something else happened. Last night, some of us got together at my brother's house. I had a phone call from my ex-husband, Bill, expressing his condolences, so I invited him and his wife to attend the spur-of-the-moment family gathering. I know Beth and Sarah you've heard me talk about how guilty I felt when Bill and I divorced thirty years ago and how I blamed myself. After dinner, we were all relating different remembrances of my father and Bill asked to stand up and read a letter he had received from my father. I was surprised and, even more so, when he shared that he and my father had communicated by letter over the years. I had no idea they had remained in contact since our divorce thirty years ago. Before he read the letter, Bill said, 'Caroline and I were so young when we were married. We weren't old enough to know what we wanted in life. In this letter, Caroline's Dad wrote that he never faulted either of us for what happened to our marriage; nor do I."

"Oh Caroline, he forgave you! I'm so happy and relieved for you that you've found so much peace from the two men who meant so much to you," Beth commented.

Two days after Caroline's 'ah-ha' moment at Wednesday night's meeting, Caroline was grateful that all of the women were seated in the front pew for her father's funeral; their presence and support offering her a soft place to land in their solidarity.

After the opening hymn and prayer, Caroline was motioned by the priest to the podium.

She carried the pamphlet she had shared on Wednesday night, and took a deep breath.

"When you are ninety-eight years old, you have much time to plan for your funeral. The biography you hold in your hand defines Dad's remarkable life and accomplishments. It's daunting to say the least! I'm going to ask however, that you put this pamphlet out of your mind for a few moments, because I prefer to remember my dad not by what he did, but by who he was. He was an incredible man in every sense of the word.

"Family was so very important. He taught us that the community of family was one of life's greatest gifts. Dad set a high standard for himself and encouraged us to do the same. As a father, he did his best to provide us with the tools we would need along the way so that my brother, sister and I could experience success in our lives. Dad taught us how to embrace the joy of accepting a challenge, appreciate the opportunity to try something new and to keep an open mind. How glorious we can all respect and acknowledge Dad's many accomplishments here on earth, yet we love and remember him for the qualities that made him the extraordinary man he was and the lessons he taught us."

Caroline continued, citing examples of each quality, sometimes sharing a humorous memory bringing quiet laughter. Often, she glanced over at the group feeling their love and support; their smiles bringing joy to her heart easing the sadness. As she closed the eulogy with the words, 'Thanks be to God', she looked directly at the women who she knew understood the double meaning of her words; her love for her dad and for them.

Jack and Beth continued to see each other until one early spring day, they were sitting in Jack's garden, when he revisited the topic neither had spoken of since viewing the photographs together.

"Beth, I've decided that, for me, the past is left in the past. I want to start our relationship fresh rather than bring the years of pain and guilt into it. I love the time we've spent together. I love it that we share some interests, both of us enjoying to write and garden. I think forty-seven years is long enough to wait. For the second time, Jack stood and walked over to kneel beside her chair. Will you marry me?"

"Yes, yes, yes! You have been in my heart most of my life. I never thought this moment would happen. I thought you were lost to me forever. Welcome home."

Beth's parents and John and Ellen were all gone leaving only Beth's children, grandchildren and the group aware of Jack's part in her past. Shortly before Ellen died, she lovingly told Beth what a difficult decision it had been to decline the offer to take the baby, but they had instead gained a sixteen-year old girl who they always thought of as their daughter.

No longer was it painful to remember the night alone in the hospital. Beth was ready to forgive her parents and appreciate that they did the best they could. It was time to let go of the pain.

When Beth told the women on Wednesday night about Jack's proposal, they were ecstatic. "The difference in your face, Beth, over the years has been remarkable." Caroline said.

"Especially in the last few months," Lexi added. "Your eyes sparkle!" Each woman hugged her and surprised her at the next meeting with a bridal shower.

At a small ceremony two months later, Beth looked out at the Wednesday group, seated in front, recognizing how much she had needed them in her life; the soft place they had provided over the years since that first year when she had shared her panic attacks and sleepless nights. Glancing over, she saw each woman with a joyous smile. Beth smiled in return; nodding her head; knowing they understood her meaning. There was little they didn't know about each other. Words weren't always necessary. They were a group of one.

Now in the twilight years of their lives, Jack and Beth wished only to enjoy their love for each other. They each continued their passion for writing, neither one writing a New York Times Best Seller, but supportive of each other's efforts.

Each Christmas, a photograph greeting card of their grandchildren arrived which they treasured, preferring to simply acknowledge with a silent hug, adding the picture to others in the drawer they had received.

Four years after Caroline's divorce, she announced with excitement and a twinkle in her eye, she had met a man named Brad, who she felt was the one, not because he reminded her of her father, nor was she attracted to him because he filled a void left by her father. He was Brad; a good man.

With the emotional support of the knitting group and work with her therapist, Lexi sought the counsel of a divorce attorney. Announcing one Wednesday night, "My attorney has assured me my husband's threats are all unfounded and, even though he has hidden the money from me for years, I am entitled to enough to not only live comfortably for the rest of my life but purchase the beach house on Martha's Vineyard I've always dreamed of owning."

The women were with her spiritually throughout the difficult divorce trial. Everyone noticed Lexi was losing weight and encouraged her, reminding her she no longer needed to use food as compensation for the degradation she felt inside.

As soon as Lexi was settled in her new home, she invited the group for the weekend where the women were pleased to meet Lexi's children. Before the next year was over, the ladies were each contributing to the knitting of a blanket they planned to give to Lexi on the birth of her first grandchild.

There was seldom silence on Wednesday night. While it appeared many of the women leaned on the group for comfort, the women enjoyed moments of laughter. One Wednesday night, Annie revealed that she had news, but was hesitant to share as she was sure the ladies would be shocked. The women stopped knitting, put their needles to rest on their laps and waiting anxiously to hear what Annie was about to reveal.

Lexi said, "Well it doesn't look like she's had a face lift!" Everyone laughed.

Jenny commented, "I don't think it's about one of her kids."

Sarah added, "Well, I'm pretty sure she's not having an affair!"

Everyone giggled as Annie stood up, turned around, lifted her shirt and revealed to the group a tattoo she had just gotten at age fifty at the base of her back. Everyone clapped at her dramatic confession. Cindy spoke for the group, assuring Annie that, despite her rash behavior, she was still a welcomed member of the group.

Epilogue

Over the years, the group shared in the joys of each woman… and there were many. When one woman announced the addition of a grandchild, the women welcomed the child as though it was an addition to the group. When a woman celebrated a child's graduation, award or accomplishment, the group celebrated as though it was a personal reflection on each woman. The women embraced each family of the other women, having heard about them for years, and now thought, "We are one family".

There was never a loss for words, an event to share or an observation during the previous week. Seldom was there silence if counsel was sought from the group. The women shared concerns they seemed to have in common; living with a husband who wasn't a communicator; the need to talk about sports or politics to generate conversations; the fact that many husbands were overwhelmed with the details their wives shared in a manner that caused only confusion and distraction for the men. The women found comfort and safety in numbers' when one or more of the women experienced some of the same frustrations with their marriages; the lack of patience, the lack of visible signs of affection and laughter, even the concerns of their diminished intimacy in the bedroom.

Yet, the women were just as quick to comment on the fine qualities of their husbands and the reasons they had fallen in love with them in the first place. Sarah spoke of how fortunate she was that her husband gave her free reign to decorate their home as she chose. Cindy related how lucky she was that her husband didn't care where they went to dinner always saying, 'Wherever you want to go is fine with me.' Annie appreciated the fact that when she raised a concern or made a suggestion to her husband, his response was more often than not, 'Whatever you think is best.' Beth's husband never ceased to be the adoring husband, daily showing his happiness with finally having Beth at his side. Caroline mentioned how much she loved her husband, Brad who was always there to help with her antique business and also took care of her car, making sure it had timely oil changes and fresh wiper blades.

The years had shown the similarities and differences in women's lives. No two woman's journey or how each had traversed it was the same. Although each woman had traveled a road in life sometimes confronted with turmoil, occasionally enduring heartache, once in a while forced to make life changing decisions, each woman now shared an inner strength, confident that they were strong enough to carry them through whatever challenges each had yet to encounter. Each woman had survived and emerged empowered. Each woman demonstrated to the others that it was possible to turn tragedies into triumphs.

Every woman, having experienced and survived their own painful journey, had developed a deep sense of compassion and understanding for the others. There was no longer anything shared in the group that would surprise the others or had not been heard before. These women exemplified the depth of some of the strongest emotions in life be they joy, anger, pain, or love.

As the group aged, so did their hands; the clicking sound of needles less pronounced than it had been years ago. A few of the women could no longer knit as they had without causing pain in their arthritic hands yet faithfully continued to attend the Wednesday night gatherings. The heart and soul of the group had strengthened simultaneously as each woman had individually grown over the past decades.

Forty years of providing support, encouragement, empathy and love had resulted in a deep-seated bond. The women never lost their need for all that Wednesday night represented. Realizing no one was capable of predicting what the future held, they continued to gather, aware of the fact that if needed, each knew where to find a soft place to land.

Made in the USA
Middletown, DE
04 August 2020

13618778R00139